ADVANCE PRAISE

"How to Surf the Waves: A Sensory and Emotional Regulation Curriculum nurturing emotional regulation! We all have different inner experiences, activities that explore and validate each person's unique experience and co-regulation, self-regulation, and sensory processing. If you are seeking to support and encourage inner diversity in a fun and meaningful way, this book is for you!"

—Kelly Mahler, OTD, OTR/L,
Author of *The Interoception Curriculum: A*
Step-by-Step Guide to Developing Mindful
Self-Regulation

". . . an engaging and affirming approach to building regulatory skills for children through the clever use of surfing as a metaphor . . . helps teachers, parents, or therapists become surf instructors and guide their surfers to learn to read the waves, find the right surfboard, and acquire the surf skills to survive the storm and avoid the sharks."

—Tracy Murnan Stackhouse, MA, OTR/L,
Executive Director,
Developmental FX, Denver, CO

". . . a valuable tool for patients, parents and families, and professionals alike!"

—Dr. Jill L. Fuini, Licensed Psychologist,
Pointe North Psychology Group

"What a fantastic way to bring self-acceptance and useful methods to those who struggle with this journey and to those who care for and about them!"

—Dr. Kathleen Adolt-Silva, EdD,
Director of the Managed Paraeducator
Program (MPP) Center of Excellence

"The resources that accompany this book are incredible—everything a teacher or therapist needs to implement the curriculum, including terrific visuals, fun videos, helpful handouts, and valuable data collections tools is included . . . An essential resource for teachers, therapists, and the individuals they support."

—Carol Burmeister, MA, Co-Author of
FLIPP the Switch* and *FLIPP the Switch 2.0

"This curriculum is a breath of fresh air in the field of sensory and emotional regulation. It combines a deep understanding of behavior with practical, accessible strategies that resonate with children of all backgrounds and abilities."

—Jessie L. Ginsburg, M.S., CCC-SLP CEO,
Pediatric Therapy Playhouse Creator,
Inside Out Sensory Certificate for SLPs
Co-Host, *Making the Shift* Live Show

"Rooted in a deep understanding of the complexities of human experience, this book emerges as a beacon of insight and practical guidance for those navigating the tumultuous seas of sensory and emotional challenges . . . Drawing from the latest research in neuroscience and psychology, DeMaria provides a solid theoretical framework that grounds the curriculum in evidence-based practices."

—Katie Karijolich, MS, OTR/L

"This is a brilliantly accessible program for multi-faceted complex challenges that can change children's lives, help individuals develop independence, and create collaborative relationships between parents, professionals, and children."

—Martha Davis,
Educational Advocate and Parent

"Dr. DeMaria has an affirming perspective throughout that allows teachers and students to develop the strategies without judgement or negativity. Dr. DeMaria's book fills the need for children with intellectual and developmental disabilities to develop tools to manage themselves which provides the building blocks for adult self-advocacy, and therefore a fulfilling life. Well done!"

—Kelly Milazzo,
President, Greenwich Autism Alliance
https://greenwichautismalliance.org/

"Finally, a program that is accessible and useful to professionals of all skill levels as well as parents and educators! You are effectively getting two books in one! In Part One, Dr. DeMaria explains complex neurodevelopmental, behavioral, and sensory concepts across multiple theories in a way that is easy to understand and integrate into practice. The curriculum in Part Two is a beautiful, multi-sensory, and dynamic program that can be taught individually or in small groups through the powerful metaphor of surfing. If you are a parent, therapist, or educator, you must have *How to Surf the Waves: A Sensory and Emotional Regulation Curriculum* in your tool box!"

—A. Peyton Moore, MA, OT, NCC, LPC
Stories Counseling and Occupational
Therapy Services, Ashland, Oregon

"As a teacher, I absolutely love how Dr. DeMaria visually shows us how to surf the waves! The curriculum is easy to follow and is extremely beneficial. The activities shown throughout the book—and how they can be completed by any age group—are fantastic. Dr. DeMaria has shown us how to help our students build regulatory skills which will carry them throughout their lives!"

—Rebecca Swingle,
Special Education Teacher

"This book was jam packed with helpful techniques and strategies. I'm looking forward to incorporating this curriculum into my resource center. The format was easy to follow. You are such an inspiration to me. You took a difficult topic and simplified it for your audience. Thank you!!"

—Vickie Mendes-Branch
Owner/Director Branching Out-
PAGE ONE RESOURCE CENTER LLC.
Parent Advocate, Mother

". . . a fresh approach to helping children and those who support them understand their feelings while building emotional regulation skills. Using an engaging surfing analogy, the author breaks down the sensory and emotional regulation program into easy-to-understand concepts."

—Amy KD Tobik,
Editor-in-Chief, *Exceptional Needs Today*
CEO, Lone Heron Publishing

How to Surf the Waves

A sensory and emotional regulation curriculum

the Waves

Tracey DeMaria, OTD, OTR/L

Edited by Rebecca Silva, Ruth Prystash, René DeLoss, and Erin Yilmaz

How to Surf the Waves: A Sensory and Emotional Regulation Curriculum
Copyright © 2024 by Tracey DeMaria

ISBN: 979-8-218-38631-3

Printed in the United States of America

Names: DeMaria, Tracey, author. | Silva, Rebecca, editor. | Prystash, Ruth, editor. | DeLoss, René, editor. | Yilmaz, Erin, editor.
Title: How to surf the waves : a sensory and emotional regulation curriculum / Tracey DeMaria ; edited by Rebecca Silva, Ruth Prystash, René DeLoss, and Erin Yilmaz.
Description: Gardner, KS : Autism Moving Forward, [2024] | Includes bibliographical references.
Identifiers: ISBN: 979-8-218-38631-3 (paperback)
Subjects: LCSH: Autistic children--Behavior modification. | Children with autism spectrum disorders--Behavior modification. | Autistic youth--Behavior modification. | Youth with autism spectrum disorders--Behavior modification. | Social interaction in children--Study and teaching. | Social interaction in adolescence--Study and teaching. | Emotional intelligence--Study and teaching. | Self-control in children--Study and teaching. | Self-control in adolescence--Study and teaching. | Adjustment (Psychology) in children--Study and teaching. | Adjustment (Psychology) in adolescence--Study and teaching. | Mindfulness (Psychology)--Study and teaching. | Autism--Life skills guides.
Classification: LCC: RJ506.A9 D46 2024 | DDC: 618.92/85882--dc23

Published by Autism Moving Forward
Gardner, KS 66030
www.autismmovingforward.com

Dedication

For my heroes,
My son, Miles, and my husband, Christopher.
Any of the good I do is always and forever for and because of you.

CONTENTS

FOREWORD

Twenty-five years ago, in a small sensory clinic in central New Jersey, I observed an occupational therapist provide a style of intervention that neuroscience would eventually confirm as a best practice. This child-led, neurodiversity-affirming occupational therapy was ahead of its time. That occupational therapist was Tracey Sutton, now Dr. Tracey DeMaria. This book, *How to Surf the Waves*, represents a quarter century of outstanding, neuroscience-informed clinical practice, packaged in an easy-to-implement format that is a tremendous resource for educators, therapists, and anyone who is interested in learning more about how regulation impacts behavior.

There isn't a single word that can describe Tracey's approach. Tracey's sessions are creative, fun, silly, authentic, empathic, crazy, hilarious, high energy when needed, calming when needed, and always child-led. Her compassion and clinical expertise are gifts to any child or professional with whom she interacts.

How to Surf the Waves is not just about understanding and developing emotional regulation skills. It's a book that tells you explicitly what to do, with activities, multi-sensory tools, and kid-friendly language that helps students understand what their body is telling them and what it needs. Full of foundational information, creative language, and effective strategies, it's a tremendous resource for anyone new to emotional regulation, while also satisfying the need of the experienced therapist or educator for something new and research-based.

It's all too common to see professionals react to a behavior without a deeper understanding that the behavior we see is just a signal that there's a problem. Despite popular opinion, the observable behavior most often isn't simply a student seeking attention or avoiding work, it's a response to stress. While the intention of these behavioral interventions is meant to be positive, the impact leads to children feeling unheard, invalidated, and judged when they are struggling. This is why *How to Surf the Waves* is such an important book at such a crucial time in education—a neuroscience-informed curriculum that offers an alternative to the behavioral interventions so often used in schools.

This book proves that all of us, especially kids with developing nervous systems, can use a lifeguard and co-regulator to help us navigate choppy waters. In the adult world, we support our friends, family, and co-workers when they're upset or struggling. We should offer that same kindness and responsiveness to our young surfers. *How to Surf the Waves* provides the framework, activities, and strategies to do just that. And it's totally awesome, dudes!

Greg Santucci, MS, OTR
Occupational Therapist
Founding Director, Power Play Pediatric Therapy

INTRODUCTION

Dear Reader,

I created this program to fill what seemed to be a void in the existing literature—a program that addressed student success and emotional wellness by helping students understand how they feel and build emotional regulation skills. This approach differs from most by treating students as partners in the therapeutic and educational process, and by viewing behaviors that may seem concerning to others as evidence of a child's attempts to adapt to the environment and support their own well-being, rather than as indicators of intentional misbehavior. This program seeks to support and affirm children's lived experiences and choices with the belief that children want to succeed and are doing their best to regulate themselves.

Rather than a traditional medical model approach that attempts to fix what is seen as "broken" or "wrong" with children, *How to Surf the Waves* aims to change that focus by providing children and the adults supporting them with an engaging and nonjudgmental way to understand and accept the diversity of their unique preferences and needs. Using a fun and engaging surfing analogy, children can explore the intensity and frequency of their feelings as part of everyday life.

Children are provided with evidence-based tools and strategies to help them surf their waves in a way that feels more personally gratifying and leads to more successful personal outcomes. As children learn to acknowledge and manage the intense feelings that, like waves, happen to each of us, they also explore how to predict and safely navigate the ever-changing waves and challenges of daily life. This program is not about changing children, but instead about supporting them as they learn to be the most satisfying version of themselves. *How to Surf the Waves* aims to normalize all feelings as part of the human experience, reminding us that we all—children and adults alike—are surfers, finding our way through the waves of life.

Tracey DeMaria
September 12, 2023

PART ONE
BEFORE YOU HEAD TO THE BEACH

Core Concepts: Diving Into Regulation

What Is Regulation?

Regulation has become an increasingly popular term for anything dealing with emotions and behavior in our society. However, it is important to know that regulation is about much more than just self-regulation of emotions and behavior. Regulation includes the processes of the whole nervous system, including impulses, behaviors, and physiological states related to sensory and body needs. Sensory, emotional, and behavioral regulation all occur separately but in conjunction with each other. Regulation abilities are also dependent on factors such as developmental level, injury, disability, and genetic makeup.

We develop regulation skills as we grow, first relying on others for help with regulation, then later developing the ability to regulate on our own. These are known, respectively, as *co-regulation* and *self-regulation*. Co-regulation involves using the support and direction of a connecting individual to help soothe and manage stressful situations. Self-regulation, on the other hand, is the ability to manage one's own behavior, thoughts, and emotions. It develops later in life.

What Is Co-Regulation?

We are all born with immature regulation abilities. Developmentally, babies are dependent on their caregivers to meet their every need—crying when they are hungry, tired, in need of changing, upset, or sick. This alerts their caregivers to meet their needs. Once the caregiver attends to the baby's needs, the baby should be better regulated. If a child remains upset, crying, and distressed, the caregiver tries different strategies, using techniques such as rocking, humming, singing, holding, pacifiers, or swaddling to soothe them. These are all types of regulation referred to as *co-regulation*.

Co-regulation remains necessary for most people throughout life. It is an important skill that helps individuals develop the regulation skills that are so critical for all humans' sense of comfort, safety, and well-being. When a person cannot achieve a regulated state, loved ones and friends can assist with varying degrees of co-regulation by using reassurance, modeling self-talk or affirmations, or providing reminders and items for regulating strategies. Some individuals may never develop mature self-regulation skills, depending on their nervous system development, related illness, or neurologic differences, and will always require co-regulation support.

What Is Self-Regulation?

Self-regulation is the ability to manage one's own behavior, thoughts, and emotions to pursue a goal or accomplish a task. It develops later in life, although some individuals may struggle to develop mature self-regulation skills as they age, depending on their nervous system development, illness, or neurologic differences. Self-regulation is dependent on a variety of cognitive and emotional skills, including: impulse control, delayed gratification, perspective taking, empathy, coping skills, stress management, self-monitoring, feedback processing, goal setting, and emotional regulation. It can also change depending on situational variables.

Children require self-regulation skills for an increasing number of situations as they grow and develop. These skills involve a number of interaction and social engagement skills, such as sharing toys, waiting, dealing with disappointment, sharing attention, and managing anger and frustration. For example, if a child is expected to wait to be called on in class, self-regulation is what helps the child sit quietly rather than calling out the answer. When a child is scared or angry, self-regulation is what helps them to manage their fear or anger, rather than escalating into a fight-or-flight response, such as yelling, fleeing, or becoming aggressive.

Why Is Regulation Important?

Our thoughts, emotions, sensory experiences, and behaviors are all essential components of our ability to meet goals or to participate in meaningful activities. In order to manage these thoughts, emotions, sensory experiences, and behaviors effectively, we must be regulated. As described above, this regulation can occur as self-regulation or as co-regulation. While self-regulation is ideal, co-regulation, or using the support and direction of a trusted individual, is a developmental first step for achieving regulation. In fact, many individuals benefit from co-regulation during times of distress.

Although there are many theoretical explanations for why regulation is necessary, the raw truth is that dysregulation is an uncomfortable feeling. Dysregulation can appear as stress or agitation, and can feel unsafe, unpleasant, isolating, and sometimes traumatic. However, there are also positive dysregulated states—moments when positive emotions are so strong that we are unable to regulate our feelings. For example, a child may be so excited about going to recess that they reach out and push their classmate. This kind of excitement can actually feel good—too good—but it becomes difficult to stay safe or make good choices when strong feelings are overwhelming us. No one can feel, think, or do their best when they are dysregulated.

Countless scenarios can cause a child to become dysregulated somewhere in the nervous system (sensory, emotions, behavior). Triggers can be sensory-based (e.g., overstimulation, aversive or unpleasant stimuli), neurologic (e.g., hyperactivity, inattention, impulsivity), or based on emotions (e.g., embarrassment, anger). Other triggers are conditioned responses stemming from previous experiences (fear, trauma, etc.). Regardless of the cause, the goal of assisting a dysregulated child is to help them feel safe and regain their ability to regulate their nervous system.

What Is Dysregulation?

The term "dysregulation" refers to difficulties or challenges in effectively processing and managing stimuli. Dysregulation can affect us on many levels, either alone or together: sensory, emotional, and behavioral. All of these challenges are related to the regulation of the individual's nervous system, specifically the autonomic nervous system. While they often co-occur, it is helpful to look at the different types of dysregulation individually.

Sensory, emotional, and behavioral dysregulation can negatively affect an individual's health and well-being. Social and academic success, self-esteem, interpersonal relationships, and leisure skill development can be greatly impacted by struggles with regulation of sensory input, emotions, and behaviors.

Sensory Dysregulation

Sensory dysregulation occurs when an individual has difficulties with the processing or modulation of sensory information from the environment or from individual responsiveness to sensory input. A person may experience over-responsiveness or under-responsiveness to sensory input from any or all of the eight senses. (Note: In this book, we talk about eight senses, rather than five—auditory, gustatory, tactile, visual, olfactory, vestibular, proprioceptive, interoceptive. For more information, see Chapter 4, Table 4.1.) Sensory dysregulation also occurs when the central nervous system cannot manage or organize itself for adaptive responses.

Sensory dysregulation impacts how the brain and body feel and can lead to emotional and behavioral dysregulation. In fact, recent research has supported links between sensory and/or emotional dysregulation with behaviors of inattention, hyperactivity, and impulsivity in children with attention deficit hyperactivity disorder (Grossman & Avital, 2023). Interoceptive sensations, such as feeling sick or hungry, can prompt a child to become emotionally dysregulated and become irritable, angry, or sad. A child who experiences sensory dysregulation due to decreased body awareness or overstimulation from noises may feel anxious and overwhelmed. Some children describe feelings of disconnection or overstimulation as feeling as if their brain is "racing" or "buzzing." Individuals may exhibit self-stimulatory behaviors, such as jumping, rocking, hand flapping, or even self-injurious behaviors, in an adaptive effort to regulate their nervous system and feel better.

Emotional Dysregulation

Emotions are a person's reactions to something they are experiencing, whether internal (such as a memory or thought) or external (such as seeing a spider or hearing people yell). Emotional regulation is the process of adapting one's emotions and resultant thoughts and behaviors to a given situation. This process involves complex neurologic, psychological, and cognitive processes. Emotional dysregulation is typically marked by difficulties in recognizing, understanding, and effectively responding to one's own emotions and the emotions of others (Paulus et al., 2021). Additionally, emotional dysregulation occurs when emotional reactions and responses are not modulated or cannot be controlled, resulting in issues such as emotional instability, rapid mood changes, and extreme reactions to emotions.

Behavioral Dysregulation

Like emotions, behavior is a response to internal or external stimuli. Behavior is more observable and can be measured more easily. For example, sadness and happiness are emotions, while crying and laughing are behaviors. Behavioral dysregulation can include a wide range of behaviors, including: shutdown, meltdown, aggression, impulsivity, inattention, and self-stimulatory behaviors. Behavioral regulation is the process of either inhibiting or activating behavior in order to achieve goals and requires a person to adaptively control their behavior. This requires a combination of cognitive processes, such as attention, working memory, and inhibitory control.

Behavioral dysregulation can be caused by emotional dysregulation but the two can also exist separately. For example, a child may be emotionally regulated but may still have trouble controlling their behavior (e.g., impulsive and inattentive behaviors, such as yelling, moving about a classroom, touching others, etc.). Conversely, a child may *appear* regulated and may display no outward signs of observable behaviors to indicate discomfort or distress, but may be experiencing significant emotional distress of many kinds, e.g., anxiety, depression, frustration, or loneliness.

What Are Meltdowns and Shutdowns?

A meltdown is an intense emotional and behavioral response to being overwhelmed or dysregulated. It is not deliberate, nor is it an attempt to manipulate or get attention. Children typically have little to no control of their actions during meltdowns.

Shutdowns are when a child becomes so distressed or overwhelmed that they withdraw into themselves and/or disengage from social interaction or activities such as speaking, eye contact, or even movement. When a non-responsive child is in a shutdown, they are not deliberately choosing to ignore or avoid.

The *How to Surf the Waves* program is designed for children with sensory, emotional, and behavioral dysregulation who are prone to meltdowns or shutdowns in which the brain is short-circuiting (so to speak) and unable to access higher thinking skills, such as reasoning, recalling past experiences or consequences, etc. *How to Surf the Waves* embraces the idea that when a huge wave of emotion hits, the only option may be to wait for it to pass, keep the child safe, and help to soothe and calm them, if possible. Children can learn to predict, minimize, and ride the stresses and challenges of daily life more smoothly, although the brain is sometimes triggered into a dysregulated state where it does not function properly. The child must get back to a place of homeostasis or calm balance before they can regain the ability to cognitively process the situation and make choices that help them feel better and enhance participation.

What Causes Dysregulation?

No single factor causes sensory, emotional, and behavioral dysregulation. In fact, multiple factors often combine to cause dysregulation. From a medical model perspective, a variety of medical or psychological diagnoses, genetic makeup, personality type, and overall reactivity style can lead to increased sensory, emotional, and behavioral regulation difficulties. From a social model view, however, factors such as abuse, trauma and other adverse childhood events, racial disparities, poverty, hunger, and housing insecurity all impact a child's ability to regulate.

It is important to move away from the idea that experiencing intense emotions and struggling to regulate is disordered and pathological, even in the face of disability or impairment. All humans will experience dysregulation at some point, though some are more prone to these experiences than others. Normalizing these experiences and providing skills and support to navigate them effectively is beneficial for improving an individual's sense of self-reliance and competency.

For certain children, biological and medical issues can prompt sensory, emotional, and behavioral struggles. This is also the case when physiological states such as fatigue, hunger, blood sugar levels, medication changes, and diet issues trigger dysregulation. Additionally, children diagnosed with seizure disorders can experience behavioral and emotional events that are prompted by neurologic changes.

Dysregulation challenges do not always stem from pathology and are an expected part of the normal human experience. Throughout a child's development, several factors impact and shape how they learn to react and behave. Everyone experiences negative emotions and distress, beginning as a baby and then developing adaptive ways to manage this distress as they grow older. This learning process—and the intensity of the distress experienced—varies greatly from one individual to another. Children's patterns of reactivity develop early in life and are affected by a number of factors, including types and intensity of distress they may experience, environmental factors, innate adaptive coping mechanisms, and the ability to self-soothe. Those with immature or diverse nervous systems can face greater difficulties in managing their sensory experiences, emotions, and behaviors. And some individuals may experience unusually strong emotions just because it is how they are wired.

The Impact of Trauma and Adverse Childhood Experiences

Childhood trauma can be caused by a wide range of experiences, including exposure to threatened or perceived danger, threats, violence, hearing about or witnessing a loved one's trauma, community trauma, car accidents, bullying, and more (De Bellis & Zisk, 2014). Trauma and other adverse childhood experiences are significant factors that can create lasting brain changes, particularly in areas responsible for sensory, emotional, and behavioral regulation (Bremner, 2022; Peverill et al., 2023). This includes but is not limited to: housing insecurity; stressors of poverty and racial disparities; family members with mental illness or substance-abuse issues; family members arrested or incarcerated; neglect; and abuse or violence in the home. In fact, recent research has brought new evidence to light that indicates racial disparities and adversities are the true root causes of a previously-believed false appearance of race-related brain structure differences (Dumornay, 2023). Essentially, racial disparities and adversities in childhood, particularly low-income factors, create changes in the brain's structures that coincide directly with the ability to regulate sensory experiences, emotions, and behaviors.

School-Based Trauma

Trauma caused by the factors listed above can impact the parts of the brain involved in sensory, emotion, and behavioral regulation. Trauma awareness in schools has improved, although this mainly involves looking at trauma from home. However, another type of trauma also affects children and is rarely discussed: school-based or school-induced trauma. Whether caused by curriculum, school discipline practices, bullying by peers or adults, fighting, weapons, violence in schools, or behavioral interventions, most school-induced trauma impacts minorities or vulnerable populations such as people of color, LGBTQIA+, neurodivergent, or disabled students.

Some specific factors that serve to traumatize students in the school setting include: use of restraint and seclusion; curriculum choices; persistent bullying; harsh or overwhelmingly punitive discipline practices; or behavioral practices that limit autonomy and access to food, movement, or regulation/ sensory tools. While many school-based trauma factors are large-scale problems that involve administrative and policy change, awareness at the educator level is a positive way to ignite ground level change. This awareness can impact student outcomes and provide both momentum and support for more systemic change (English et al., 2023; Hancock & Richardson, 2022; Powell, 2020).

The Role of Instructors, Parents, and Caregivers

Parenting/caregiving and teaching style play a role in children's emotional and behavioral health. It is a vast subject and the focus of countless books and research. Both parenting and teaching styles can help or hinder a child's ability to navigate the ups and downs of their day. Parenting and teaching styles that are abusive, neglectful, belittling, fear-evoking, overprotective, or demeaning can prompt or intensify difficulties with behavior and emotional functioning in a child. These approaches occur in schools, just as they do in homes. Every child is different, and every situation is different, but some basic principles do characterize relationship styles. Building relationships through understanding, compassion, and collaboration are the hallmark of effective parenting and teaching styles. As Dr. Ross W. Greene (2010) points out, kids do well if they can.

When Does Dysregulation Require Support?

When a child experiences feelings of dysregulation in their brain or body, dysregulation challenges may arise. These challenges can be mild, causing the individual discomfort, or severe, putting the individual at risk. When a child struggles with regulation, they are less available to learn and function because too much brain power, attention, and energy is spent managing and coping with strong sensory experiences, emotions, and related behaviors. They are more likely to face disciplinary consequences, such as restraint, seclusions, and suspension, which further limits their access to education and social engagement. Children do not want to feel dysregulated or unsuccessful at managing their emotions and behaviors. Given the proper support and opportunity for success, they will do what they are capable of to feel better.

Listening to the first-person accounts of neurodivergent individuals, who frequently experience dysregulation, shows that periods of extreme dysregulation, especially when prolonged or repeated, are traumatic. Trauma occurs when an individual experiences threatening or harmful physical or emotional events that have lasting negative effects. Such traumatic experiences are often characterized by feeling a loss of control. Being severely dysregulated is scary, feels threatening, and often causes harm (either physically through self-injury or emotionally). There is a strong feeling of not being in control during these times. A recent study discusses the impact of conflicts between autistic characteristics and the environment as a cause of sensory trauma (Kerns et al., 2022).

What Are Dysregulation Challenges?

Sometimes dysregulation interferes with activities or impairs a child's ability to function to their potential, but is not imminently dangerous to the child or others. It is always important to consider the severity and impact of a behavioral challenge.

It is important to understand that some behaviors, though considered atypical by some, are self-protective and necessary for the regulation, well-being, and safety of the child. For example, hand-flapping or rocking back and forth may look odd to some people, but may actually be how an individual calms themself. Every child adapts to their feelings differently. What is distressing for some may be beneficial for others. For example, some behaviors, such as special interests (or what some people label as "fixations"), can be areas of great strength for individuals. Reshaping the professional frame of thinking about behavior is an important part of understanding and supporting students.

What Are Dysregulation Challenges That May Require Support?

Determining the impact of a behavior on *the autonomy and needs of the child* is necessary to determine whether the challenge requires some type of support. If a child is simply not complying, or if a behavior is outside of what an adult considers the norm, it is not necessarily something that requires intense and immediate intervention.

Some children experience times of getting stuck in a behavior or pattern and need assistance to get unstuck. For example, if a child is hyper-focused on the need for a certain ritual or routine, this can increase anxiety or distress and impact self-care for the child in terms of activities such as eating and sleeping. Therefore, providing compassionate support through accepting variations and changes can be beneficial for the child's internal sense of well-being. What is crucial is to determine what is best for the child, rather than what is best for everyone else. Table 1.1 describes dysregulation challenges that might require some support.

Dysregulation Challenges That May Require Some Support

- Avoidance, escape, or fleeing from stressful situations: crawling under desk, running out of a room
- Shutdown: unable to talk, interact, engage, or perform due to distress
- Compulsions: checking and rechecking tasks or completed work, hoarding items, constantly seeking reassurance
- Rigid adherence to certain routines or rituals
- Hyper- or hypoactivity: having intensely high persistent activity level or equally low, lethargic activity level
- Intense sensory sensitivities and/or sensory-seeking behaviors: severe avoidance of one or more type of sensory input (unable to wear shoes/clothes, or eat solid food) or needing too much input (constant need for intense movement or body input, such as grinding teeth excessively, crashing unsafely into items, eating non-food items)
- Mild forms of self-injurious behavior, such as biting nails or pulling on or pulling out hair

Table 1.1. Description of dysregulation challenges that may require some support

When Does Dysregulation Require Maximum Support?

When a child experiences intense, overwhelming, and disruptive feelings in their brain or body, extreme dysregulation challenges may arise. These challenges can be internalized (e.g., depression and anxiety) or externalized (e.g., meltdowns, aggression). Table 1.2 shows examples of dysregulation challenges that are concerning in all contexts and circumstances, as these behaviors can cause emotional or physical harm to self or others.

Dysregulation Challenges That Require Maximum Support

- Physical aggression: hitting, kicking, pushing, spitting, biting, scratching, pulling hair
- Verbal aggression: insulting, harassing
- Destruction of property: throwing and breaking things, punching walls, ripping up property of others
- Self-injurious behavior: intense head-banging, extreme hitting, or scratching self
- Self-mutilation: biting fingers, pulling out hair, cutting

Table 1.2. Description of dysregulation challenges that require maximum support

How Can Both Pleasant and Unpleasant Feelings Cause Dysregulation Challenges?

Both pleasant and unpleasant (positive and negative) emotions can cause a variety of behaviors, although behaviors are almost always interpreted in a negative way. For example, if a child is laughing hysterically, adults may assume—erroneously—that the child is happy, seeking attention, or thinks something is funny, whereas in reality the child is excessively dysregulated.

Emotions and behaviors are both developmental and individual; they emerge and exist in conjunction with but separate from one another. There is no specific formula for understanding which emotion will prompt a specific behavior in each situation or individual. Just as some intense emotions can be experienced without obvious behavioral manifestations, some potentially concerning behaviors, such as impulsivity, are not typically dependent on emotions.

Poor regulation of positive emotions can lead to behavioral dysregulation. Examples of pleasant emotions or feelings and possible resulting behaviors that might require some support are shown in Figure 1.1. Examples of distressing feelings and emotions and possible resulting behaviors are shown in Figure 1.2.

Dysregulation Challenges Caused by Positive or Pleasant Feelings and Emotions

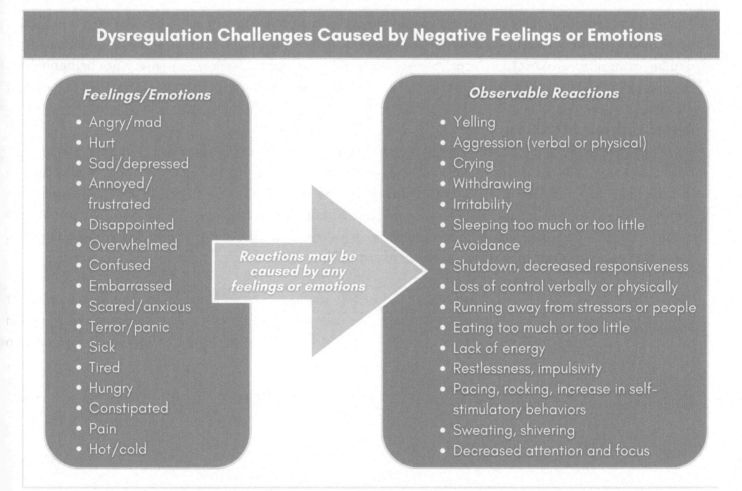

Feelings/Emotions

- Excitement
- Anticipation
- Silliness/giddiness
- Elation/joy
- Euphoria
- Happiness

Reactions may be caused by any feelings or emotions

Observable Reactions

- Special interests (fixations)
- Inattention, distraction
- Distracting behaviors (making noises, fidgeting)
- Restlessness, laughter
- Unsafe, impulsive movements that can lead to injury
- Speaking too loudly, talking too much
- Out of control or unsafe physical behaviors

Figure 1.1. Dysregulation challenges that may be caused by positive or pleasant feelings and emotions

Dysregulation Challenges Caused by Negative Feelings or Emotions

Feelings/Emotions

- Angry/mad
- Hurt
- Sad/depressed
- Annoyed/frustrated
- Disappointed
- Overwhelmed
- Confused
- Embarrassed
- Scared/anxious
- Terror/panic
- Sick
- Tired
- Hungry
- Constipated
- Pain
- Hot/cold

Reactions may be caused by any feelings or emotions

Observable Reactions

- Yelling
- Aggression (verbal or physical)
- Crying
- Withdrawing
- Irritability
- Sleeping too much or too little
- Avoidance
- Shutdown, decreased responsiveness
- Loss of control verbally or physically
- Running away from stressors or people
- Eating too much or too little
- Lack of energy
- Restlessness, impulsivity
- Pacing, rocking, increase in self-stimulatory behaviors
- Sweating, shivering
- Decreased attention and focus

Figure 1.2. Dysregulation challenges that may be caused by negative feelings or emotions

11

Why Do Labels Matter? Maladaptive Versus Dysregulated

The term maladaptive behavior has long been used to describe concerning behaviors. Maladaptive refers to behaviors that do not allow a person to adapt to a situation or to behaviors that are harmful. This term can cause confusion and misguide, as it is often applied to any behavior that is not considered "typical" or "appropriate." It implies that the behaviors do not help meet an individual's need to adapt and accomplish a goal. For example, a child who shuts down (stops talking, covers their ears, or hides) may be using these behaviors to self-regulate when overstimulated by sensory or emotional experiences. The withdrawal can appear maladaptive, but may actually be a child's way of preventing sensory distress or emotions from intensifying and ultimately leading to verbal or physical aggression.

The term "maladaptive" is avoided in this program. While a specific behavior may be problematic for some individuals, for others it may not. For example, self-stimulatory behaviors may not be considered typical behavior by neurotypical individuals, but they often serve the function of helping a neurodivergent individual adapt to internal stressors and tolerate and adapt to uncomfortable situations.

As humans, we can tolerate distress in one situation or time, but when given a different environment, time of day, or set of circumstances, the distress may be more difficult to tolerate. It is important to evaluate each situation individually before deciding whether immediate support is needed.

As these issues often affect neurodivergent individuals, it is critical to listen to the voices of neurodivergent individuals to best understand how to effectively build adaptive sensory, emotional, and behavioral regulation skills. All people have different nervous system responsivity. What is adaptive for one child may be distressing to another. Everyone adapts differently.

A Note about Masking

Masking is when a person consciously or unconsciously hides or suppresses their thoughts, feelings, or characteristics to conform to societal expectations or to protect themselves. This often results in a discrepancy between what is outwardly expressed and the internal experience. Masking can increase stress and decrease a true sense of self. Although masking may occur in all people, it is a serious concern for neurodivergent individuals, who are often taught or shamed into behaving in ways that conceal their true selves in order to "fit in."

CHAPTER TWO

The Brain: The Nerve Center of Surfing

Sensory experiences, emotions, and behaviors stem from structures and functions in the brain and the nervous system. They cannot be separated. The brain is the birthplace of how we learn, think, and feel. The world around us travels into our brain through neuron and nerve pathways. We make sense of the world in our brain. Everything we see, hear, taste, smell, and feel gets processed in the brain. Situations are understood or interpreted, plans are made and executed—all within mere milliseconds. There are processes within the brain that occur simultaneously: electrical (neurons and axons), chemical (neurotransmitters), and metabolic (glucose). These processes all impact the various functions of the brain, including arousal level, motor control, learning and memory, motivation, and perception.

Sensory experiences, emotions, and behaviors are core functions of the brain, which are part of a complex and interconnected process. It is not necessary to understand the complexity of neuroanatomy and neurophysiology to understand and support positive changes in the brain that assist with sensory, emotional, and behavioral regulation. However, it helps to have a basic idea of the structures and function of the brain. This awareness is especially beneficial for those working to understand neurodivergence, as well as the basic premise that emotions and behaviors are far more complex than just being "naughty" or "odd." Simply telling a child to calm down or attempting to control behavior without understanding the reasons or function of these behaviors can be ineffective and even harmful. To understand the brain's role in the *How to Surf the Waves* program, and in emotions and behaviors generally, the following are some basic useful terms.

Brain Structures—Location and Function

Cerebrum: Contains four lobes (frontal, temporal, parietal, occipital) and is divided into left and right hemispheres. Considered the information processing center. Responsible for brain functions such as sensation, memory, speech/language, voluntary movement, emotion, behavior, and more. (*See Figure 2.1.*)

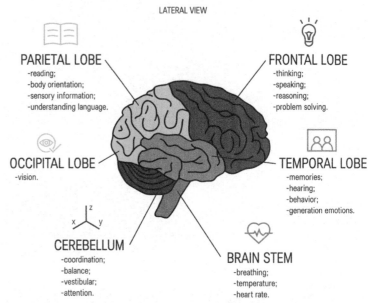

FUNCTIONAL AREAS OF THE BRAIN
LATERAL VIEW

PARIETAL LOBE
-reading;
-body orientation;
-sensory information;
-understanding language.

FRONTAL LOBE
-thinking;
-speaking;
-reasoning;
-problem solving.

OCCIPITAL LOBE
-vision.

TEMPORAL LOBE
-memories;
-hearing;
-behavior;
-generation emotions.

CEREBELLUM
-coordination;
-balance;
-vestibular;
-attention.

BRAIN STEM
-breathing;
-temperature;
-heart rate.

Figure 2.1. Brain structure

1) **Frontal lobe:** Performs thinking, decision-making, and planning.

2) **Temporal lobe:** Processes auditory information, aspects of memory, emotions, and behavior.

3) **Parietal lobe:** Processes sensory information related to touch, taste, and temperature; contains sensory motor cortex, language processing.

4) **Occipital lobe:** Processes visual information.

5) **Cerebellum:** A structure in the back of the brain under the cerebrum that controls motor functions, such as coordination, balance, equilibrium, and posture.

6) **Brain stem:** The bottom stalk-like part of the brain that controls basic functions of the body, including heart rate, breathing, and sleep. It connects the spinal cord to the cerebellum.

Terminology and Functional Brain Concepts

The following are some common terms and concepts frequently used for understanding the interconnectedness of sensations, emotions, thoughts, and behaviors in the brain.

- **The limbic system:** Located in the cerebrum, it is composed of multiple structures, including the amygdala and the hippocampus (the area of the brain responsible for emotion, learning, motivation, and memory). It links the cortex or cortical (thinking) areas with the more unconscious brain stem areas. Controls response to intense emotion (e.g., fight or flight).

- **Subcortical:** This term relates to the brain's structures and to functions that are more primitive and autonomic, e.g., limbic system structures, cerebellum, and brainstem functions (heart rate, breathing).

- **Prefrontal cortex:** The front part of the frontal lobe. It is a complex thinking area responsible for executive functions (attention, self-control, working memory, etc.), decision-making, social behavior, and personality. It is located just behind the forehead.

- **Top-down:** Refers to the process of using the cortical or thinking processes to impact the subcortical processes. An example is using intention and thinking to guide behavior and internal states of emotion or arousal.

- **Bottom-up:** Refers to the concept of stimulating or using subcortical processes, which are based on sensory or motor input received in the more primitive brain structures, to impact the higher cortical areas of the brain. For example, when a person is swinging on a swing, the movement immediately impacts their brain to create a calm emotional state.

- **Arousal:** Being *aware* and stimulated in the brain—emotionally, physically, or cognitively.

- **Arousal level** (in relation to learning, attention, performance): Range or degree of alertness or stimulation as needed for optimal performance, attention, and learning.

- **Homeostasis:** An equilibrium or balance among different organisms or functions in the brain (e.g., body temperature, sleep-wake cycles, appetite, hormones, etc.). It is when the physiological aspects of the brain are at ease. This is when we are "in the zone" and available to learn and participate in life most effectively.

What Is the Emotional Brain?

The limbic system structures are considered to be the emotional brain and are believed to be the area of the brain responsible for emotional control. This area is composed of structures located in the center of the brain, behind the frontal cortex. The amygdala, hippocampus, cingulate cortex, and orbitofrontal cortex are universally agreed to be the structures that regulate and control emotions (Rolls, 2019).

- **The amygdala** is responsible for emotional reactivity, memory, and some aspects of decision-making. The amygdala sends and receives information via connections to various structures of the brain. There is a significant connection between the amygdala and fear conditioning and memories.

- **The hippocampus** plays a key role in memory, especially new memories about events and experiences, and some aspects of long-term, short-term, and special memory. It is also thought to play a role in forming social memories and perceiving the emotions of others (Immordino-Yang & Singh, 2013).

- **The limbic system** is responsible for emotional states, including fear and anger, as well as the hormonal and chemical reactions to emotional states. The structures of the limbic system are also believed to play a role in functions such as emotional memory, behavior, long-term memory, olfaction (smell), sexual behaviors, addiction, sleep, dreams, appetite, and emotional regulation of eating, motivation, and social processing/cognition (RajMohan & Mohandas, 2007).

What Is the Thinking Brain?

The thinking part of the brain is primarily located in the cerebrum or cerebral cortex, directly behind the forehead, in the frontal lobe of the brain. The thinking part of the brain is responsible for cognition and what we refer to as *thinking*, or the mental processes that are responsible for knowledge and how we learn. Cognitive skills involve intellectual effort and are responsible for information-processing and high-level processes such as thinking, reasoning, planning, comprehension, problem-solving, voluntary movements, and some components of language. Cognitive skills can be categorized into attention, memory, visual and spatial, language, and executive function skills.

What Are Executive Function Skills?

Executive function skills is an umbrella term used to describe cognitive processes and self-regulation skills. Self-regulation weakness or delays are often present in children with emotional and behavioral dysregulation.

Executive function skills include:
- **Planning and organization:** Ability to decide on a goal and systematically plan how to accomplish it.

- **Impulse control:** Behavioral inhibition and thinking before acting.

- **Flexible thinking:** Adapting to the unexpected, ability to shift smoothly from one situation to another.

- **Emotional control:** Ability to react appropriately to a given situation, keeping emotions in check.

- **Working memory:** Ability to keep important information in the forefront of the mind for functional use.

- **Self-monitoring:** Ability to self-evaluate with accuracy in a given situation.

While executive function skills are cognitive/thinking processes, they are also interdependent on communication with the emotional brain and are shown to be linked with emotional regulation skills (Hendricks & Buchanan, 2016). These executive function skills allow us to perform complex tasks, such as focusing attention, multi-tasking, remembering instructions, planning multistep activities, and organizing needed materials.

It is because of this established link in cognitive processes and emotional and behavioral regulation that the *How to Surf the Waves* curriculum aims to build aspects of executive functioning skills. The key executive function skills addressed in this curriculum include emotional control, flexible thinking, self-monitoring, and behavioral inhibition.

What Is the Relationship Between the Emotional Brain and the Thinking Brain?

While there is a distinction between the emotional and the thinking parts of the brain, they are interconnected and work together symbiotically, each one impacting and reacting to the other. The emotional brain includes structures that stimulate automatic body reactions (breathing, heart rate, sweating) and fight-or-flight mechanisms of the nervous system. The emotional brain triggers automatic reactions, often without ever needing to communicate with the thinking part of the brain, especially for children with emotional and behavioral regulation difficulties. For some children, the pathways that override emotional responses with higher-level thinking processes are underdeveloped or impaired.

When the emotional part of the brain is stimulated and active (such as in a meltdown or moment of significant distress), many children are unable to access the thinking part of their brain. This lack of interaction between the thinking and emotional brain is why children in heightened emotional states are unable to cognitively reason through a situation or predict the consequences of their behaviors in the moment. They are acting without thinking because they literally cannot think at a higher level in the given moment. For children who have difficulty with the interaction between their thinking and emotional brain, building and strengthening these pathways and connections becomes an important goal of intervention and for improving the behavioral control of emotional states.

If a child has difficulty with the functioning of their emotional brain, one may see frequent overreactions with high intensity, frequency, and/or duration of distress. Dysfunction in the emotional brain can be present for any number of reasons, from autism to anxiety to environmental factors. *When a child is having an emotional brain reaction, they will be unable to fully process thinking brain concepts such as consequences or verbal appeals to calm down.* Because of this difficulty with communication between the emotional and cognitive parts of the brain when a person is dysregulated, it is critical to learn what may trigger or prompt dysregulation and practice coping and adaptive skills when in a calm or regulated state.

Connecting the Thinking and Emotional Brain

There are multiple roads or pathways that connect the various structures and nuclei of the limbic system with the cortex. These pathways involve communication via neurons. In a neurotypical brain, the emotional brain, though it can act or react alone, is thought to be controlled in part by the thinking brain. However, when these pathways or structures are underdeveloped or impaired, this back-and-forth communication is adversely impacted.

Developmentally, the emotional brain matures earlier and more rapidly than the thinking brain. In fact, the pre-frontal cortex is the last part of the brain to fully develop and is still growing into the third decade of life (Hochberg, 2011). This explains why children and adolescents are more motivated by emotions and impulses than adults, with less ability to inhibit or control behaviors. This underdeveloped interaction between the two areas is the reason why an older child in a rational and calm state might be able to identify good, positive choices and coping skills, *but in the moment*, when distressed or motivated by emotion and impulse, they make a choice that demonstrates poor judgment. While this immaturity in the connections between the thinking and emotional brain is true for all children and adolescents, it is more prominent and prolonged for children with emotional and behavioral regulation difficulties stemming from atypical neurologic and psychologic functioning. This does not mean that children with more pronounced immaturity in these mechanisms cannot learn to improve communication between their thinking and emotional brains. But it likely does mean that they will require practice and instruction.

Distress and Distress Tolerance

Distress is a term generally used to describe pain or suffering—emotional or physical—and other negative emotions, such as anxiety or anger. Distress tolerance is the ability to tolerate, cope with, and manage distressing emotions and situations. It requires a person to regulate internal emotional states in response to perceived or actual stress or discomfort. The term "distress tolerance" refers here to a specific element of intervention aimed at helping individuals who experience intense emotions. Distress tolerance is not a skill that is fully developed at birth. Think of babies and their instinct to cry when they are hungry, tired, sick, or scared. This lack of distress tolerance is developmentally critical for babies to get their needs met. As children age and their brains mature, their tolerance to distress ought to mature as they grow. However, just as people can have varying levels of emotional sensitivity, they can also have innately varying degrees of distress tolerance.

For children with sensory, emotional, and behavioral dysregulation, especially those who are neurodivergent, this ability to tolerate distress is often immature or underdeveloped. Distress, whether physiological or emotional, is at the root of many potentially concerning behaviors that impact a child's daily life. For some, feeling overwhelmed by an undesired task or sensory stimuli causes severe distress, so they seek to avoid the situation. While these behaviors are considered problematic by many professionals, avoiding distressing situations is the brain's attempt at an adaptive response to distress. This is a good example of how a situation can be interpreted negatively when the root cause is misunderstood.

Building tolerance to distress takes practice. If not done correctly, it can create trauma. It is important to teach a child that feeling some degree of distress is a normal part of life for most people, such as the smell of other people in a crowd or the sound of people eating at mealtime. The child can learn to tolerate these with sensory and emotional supports, although it is imperative to do this with the child's consent. Maybe a child can learn to cope with the distress of loud noises when given noise-reducing headphones, or they can bring a scented item they enjoy when they must deal with crowds, to compete with unpleasant odors.

The most important application of this concept is to help a child tolerate distress for essential life functions. For example, learning to tolerate the physical discomfort of toothbrushing is a critical skill, as complete avoidance of oral care can lead to medical complications. Modeling by adults and being given guidance through distress (assurance, sensory strategies, advanced warning, and preparedness) can help children learn how to better tolerate the feelings of distress when necessary. Allowing a child to build this tolerance with an empathetic, trusted, and safe adult can be critical to developing life skills that are necessary for independence and fulfillment in later years.

Important note: This should not be mistaken for teaching a child that they need to accept or tolerate all types and degrees of distress. It is important to honor the child's internal experience and allow a voice and control.

Blending Top-Down and Bottom-Up Concepts

How to Surf the Waves uses a variety of strategies to help support the individual needs of children with sensory, emotional, and behavioral dysregulation. Many tools, interventions, and strategies rely on a single premise or skill. Blending the concepts of top-down and bottom-up processing is how cognitive and thinking skills, as well as body and sensory input, can impact regulation, emotions, and behaviors.

Top-down refers to the process of using the cortical/thinking processes to impact the subcortical processes of the body and sensory systems (*See Figure 2.2*). For example, if a child does not want to lose recess time (an antiquated and harmful practice) and tries to regulate their behaviors to not call out or get out of their seat, they are using intention and thinking to guide behavior and internal states of arousal. They may use self-affirmations, self-monitoring, or cognitive distractions to help them regulate their bodies or behaviors.

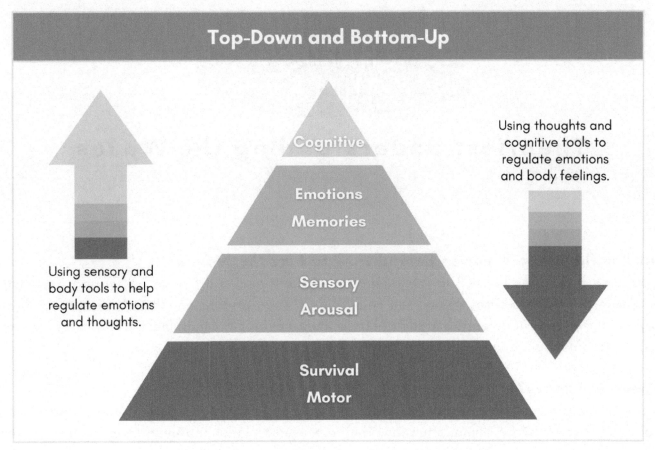

Figure 2.2. Regulating emotions using sensory and cognitive tools

Bottom-up, on the other hand, refers to the low order or subcortical processes that are based on body and sensory input received in the bottom brain structures. An example of this is to use exercise or eat a snack, not talking about the issue that is causing distress, and waiting for the input from these to regulate the nervous system.

This bottom-up and top-down process also occurs when a person sees an image or hears a sound that is immediately perceived as a threat, and the brain reacts automatically. When experiencing distress (fear, upset, anger, etc.), these emotional states can impact the nervous system, causing physiological reactions. Similarly, nervous system distress that stems from physiological states or experiences, such as sensory input, can have an equal impact on emotional states and behavior. The top and bottom brain areas have also been referred to as the "upstairs and downstairs brain" (Siegel & Bryson, 2011, as cited in Santucci, 2023).

Theories: Understanding the Waves

What Are the Basic Theories Behind *How to Surf the Waves*?

The grounding theories utilized in the *How to Surf the Waves* curriculum are varied and include developmental theory, arousal theory, self-regulation theory, attachment theory, sensory integration theory, cognitive behavior theory, and their related therapies: yoga, mindfulness-based stress reduction (MBSR), and dialectical behavior therapy (DBT).

What Is Theory?

Theories help guide professionals, based on the collective works and agreed-upon understandings of others working in a similar situation. They are used to influence every stage of intervention—from assessment and evaluation to the choice and administration of services or supports. A theory provides some measure of assurance that someone else has used a similar technique before for the equivalent situation, and it produced a desired outcome. Theories are used in healthcare professions, educational professions, social sciences, psychology, and more. There are some basic theories that crossover between professions, while some are unique to individual professions.

For occupational therapists, psychologists, Speech-Language Pathologists (SLP), and other therapists, theory provides a framework for professionals to develop clinical reasoning. *Clinical reasoning* takes us beyond just knowing what intervention and strategies to use; it is the process that therapists use to determine *why* they are choosing a particular strategy, where to go next, and what to do if a strategy does not work. Therapists can use the same tools or strategies but may have quite different clinical reasoning behind why they are using it for a particular child in a specific situation. For instance, one therapist may choose to have a child play with shaving cream to decrease their nervous system arousal level and improve attention, while another therapist may use shaving cream play for a different child to provide soothing tactile sensory input and cognitive distraction to lower anxiety.

Sensory Integration Theory

Sensory integration theory, pioneered by occupational therapist and neuropsychologist, Dr. A. Jean Ayers, is a framework that explains how the brain processes and integrates sensory information from our surroundings to form a cohesive understanding of the world (Bundy et al., 2002). When sensory input is properly received and integrated, it promotes adaptive responses (purposeful effective actions), efficient motor skills, emotional regulation, and overall well-being.

Sensory integration theory includes several key concepts. First, it recognizes that the central nervous system has plasticity and can change over time. Second, sensory integration is a developmental process that evolves as we grow, indicating that we are not born with fully mature sensory integration abilities. Third, the theory highlights the interdependence between high-order (cortical) and low-order (subcortical) functions in the brain, emphasizing their integrated functioning. Sensory integration is not synonymous with sensory stimulation, sensory-based strategies, sensory preferences, or sensory sensitivity (Bundy & Murray, 2002; Schaaf, 2003). See the *Common Sensory Terms* chart (Table 3.1).

Common Sensory Terms	
Sensory Integration	Taking information from the basic senses (auditory, visual, gustatory, olfactory, vestibular, proprioceptive, tactile, and interoceptive), processing the information, making sense of it, and responding to it.
Sensory Integration Theory	The theory, based on the work of A. Jean Ayres, provides a framework that explains how the brain processes and integrates sensory information from our surroundings to form a cohesive understanding of the world.
Ayers Sensory Integration® (ASI)	An evidenced-based intervention used when the sensory integration theory is applied by specially trained professionals. Intervention must meet specific parameters, including delivery in the context of play, a sensory-rich environment, individualized assessment, child-therapist collaboration, and specific therapeutic activities to promote sensory integration (Lane et al., 2019).
Sensory Processing Dysfunction	When a child has impaired sensory processing abilities. Sometimes occurs in isolation but often is seen with other diagnoses or issues, most commonly autism.
Sensory-Based Strategies	The use of sensory and motor-based tools and/or techniques to assist a child in achieving and maintaining a desired outcome, e.g., sitting on ball chairs to increase attention or posture, using soft/gentle music to calm, chewing gum to stay alert. Synonymous with sensory integration theory.
Sensory Diet	Sensory diet is a commonly used term to describe a personalized set of sensory activities or strategies designed to meet an individual's sensory needs and promote self-regulation. Also synonymous with sensory integration therapy.

Table 3.1. Glossary of common sensory terms

Individuals possess an innate drive to develop their sensory integration skills. Adaptive responses play a crucial role in sensory integration, as they facilitate the integration of sensory input. These foundational principles provide the basis for child-directed, play-based interventions that offer just-right challenges in a safe environment. Sensory-motor input and a variety of activities are adjusted as needed, allowing for desired adaptive responses and providing opportunities for success (Bundy et al., 2002; Schaaf & Miller, 2005).

Ayers Sensory Integration® (ASI®) has been proven effective in enhancing self-care, socialization, and goal attainment for children with autism. ASI® intervention should be provided by a specially trained occupational therapist in a sensory-rich environment with individualized assessment, child-therapist collaboration, and specific therapeutic activities to promote sensory integration (Kilroy et al., 2019).

Sensory integration theory and ASI intervention were initially intended to improve the sensory-motor, learning, and advanced planning skills of children with sensorimotor and learning problems, particularly those under the age of 10. The theory was not originally developed with children of older ages or those with complex neurologic, psychological, genetic, or medical challenges in mind. Sensory integration theory has since been expanded and used to guide the development and use of sensory-based interventions, or sensory strategies, for many neurodivergent individuals, as well as older children and even adults.

Cognitive-Behavioral Theory

Cognitive-behavioral theory is a framework of beliefs used by a variety of allied professionals, from psychologists to social workers and occupational therapists, and supports the idea that there is a connection between thoughts, emotions, and behaviors. The most significant contributors to the theory are Aaron Beck and Albert Ellis, though relevant contributions and supportive evidence continue to occur from other researchers. Cognitive-behavioral theory submits that behavioral and cognitive approaches should be combined to address psychological issues. It recognizes that cognition, affect, and behavior are interconnected yet distinct aspects of human experience.

Cognitive-behavioral theory acknowledges that thoughts can significantly influence behavior and that thoughts and beliefs can gradually be modified to bring about behavioral changes. By challenging negative or irrational thoughts, individuals can reshape their behavior and improve their emotional well-being. Cognitive-behavioral theory recognizes that emotions and feelings are dependent on one's beliefs and knowledge. It also acknowledges that human development is influenced by cognitive interaction, learned behaviors, and the environment (Norcross et al., 2016; Nurius & Macy, 2008).

Cognitive Behavioral Therapy (CBT), which is derived from cognitive-behavioral theory, has been studied and proven to be an effective, evidenced-based intervention across a variety of ages and psychological issues, including those that impact health and wellness, such as pain management and insomnia (Selvanathan et al., 2021). CBT is regularly used with children to address issues of health and wellness, from anxiety to obesity. More recently, CBT has been adapted and shown to be effective with autistic children for improved emotional regulation and engagement (Lee et al. 2022). To effectively implement CBT, a trusting and collaborative relationship between the therapist and the client and/or family is essential. There should be open communication and shared decision-making throughout the therapeutic process (Norcross et al., 2016). This collaborative aspect of CBT, when properly adhered to, can lend itself well to being a used in a neurodiversity-affirming manner.

Arousal Theory

Arousal theory originates from psychologists Robert M. Yerkes and John Dillingham Dodson and suggests there is an optimal level of physiological or brain arousal one must achieve for effective task performance. It proposes that arousal level should be neither too high nor too low. Brain arousal levels are closely connected to stress and performance, with a complex interplay between these functions. Arousal refers to levels of being awake and alert and able to attend. Emotional arousal, though specifically triggered by emotions, meaning, or memories, also is a function of the brain that occurs at a physiological level, specifically a result of the autonomic nervous system. For example, if a child experiences a negative emotion, the autonomic nervous system reacts and increases the arousal level in the brain. This increase in response or arousal to emotions is measured by physiological functions such as heart rate (Zantinge et al., 2017). For children who are neurodivergent or have immature and not fully developed nervous systems, arousal levels are frequently impacted. Understanding of arousal theory is important when working with children who experience sensory and emotional dysregulation because these states of dysregulation are inextricably linked to arousal levels.

Sensory Modulation Theory

Sensory modulation is a theory and practice framework that stems from sensory integration theory. Sensory modulation was initially considered the ability to process sensory input correctly for appropriate responses (Bundy et al., 2002). But the definition evolved over time to include regulation, considering sensory modulation as, ". . . a twofold process. It originates in the central nervous system as the neurological ability to regulate and process sensory stimuli; this subsequently offers the individual an opportunity to respond behaviourally to the stimulus" (Brown et al., 2019, p. 521). It is the aspect of sensory processing that includes the popular concepts of sensory sensitivity, sensory avoidance, and sensory-seeking behaviors, which are unfortunately sometimes misunderstood to be either-or concepts. For example, if a child is sensitive to oral sensory or taste information, a person may perhaps incorrectly assume they are sensitive to all sensory input.

True sensory modulation happens on a continuum, where people tend to fluctuate between over- and under-responsiveness to sensory input, the environment, or other circumstances surrounding the input. Sensory modulation also stresses the importance of providing sensory experiences that are individually tailored to meet the person's sensory needs, helping them achieve an optimal level of arousal and regulation. Awareness of sensory modulation and strategies to support it are important in the *How to Surf the Waves* curriculum.

Additionally, arousal levels of the nervous system can impact sensory modulation abilities. If the nervous system is not in an optimal arousal state, it may not process information correctly. With impaired sensory modulation, a person may, for example, hear an unexpected knock on the door or crash of a dish in a sink and perceive this sound as equal in intensity and threat to a fire alarm, causing the nervous system to send a rush of chemicals, the same rush of chemicals it would send to alert the brain and body to danger. The person may react in a disproportionate manner, possibly screaming, fleeing the room, and/or covering their ears. Managing arousal levels and sensory modulation abilities is an important part of helping a child manage their emotions and behaviors throughout their day.

Table 3.2, *Essential Theories Behind How to Surf the Waves*, explains basic tenets, common features, and characteristics of several theories that are foundational for the program.

Essential Theories Behind *How to Surf the Waves*		
Sensory Integration Theory	**Cognitive-Behavioral Theory**	**Arousal Theory**
• The central nervous system is plastic (can change) • Sensory integration develops; we are not born with mature sensory integration • The brain functions as an integrated whole: high-order (cortical) and low-order (subcortical) functions are interdependent on and impact each other • Adaptive responses are critical to sensory integration • People have an inherent drive to develop sensory integration (Bundy et al., 2002)	• Combines behavioral and cognitive approaches • Cognitions and behavior are different • Thoughts can impact behavior • Thoughts and beliefs can be changed through a gradual process • Changing your thoughts can change your behavior • Emotions and feelings are dependent on beliefs and knowledge	• An optimal level of nervous system arousal is needed for performance • Arousal should be neither too high nor too low • For children with immature nervous systems, or those with impaired nervous systems (due to medical, genetic, or psychological diagnoses), arousal levels can be negatively impacted (Communication Theory, n.d.) • Increase in response or arousal to emotions can measured by physiological functions such as heart rate (Zantinge et al., 2017)
Common features/characteristics of theory		
• Child-directed, play-based • Just-right challenge • Safe environment • Sensory-motor input • Variety of activities adjusted as needed • Desired adaptive responses • Opportunities for success (Schaff & Miller, 2005)	• Development results from cognitive interaction, learned behaviors, and environment • Trusting collaborative relationship between therapist and client/family is essential (Norcross et al., 2016)	• In a heightened state of arousal, person may be very reactive to small quantities or intensities of sensory information • A low arousal level may need more sensory input to register it
Therapies/techniques derived from the theories		
• Ayers Sensory Integration® (ASI) • Primarily used by occupational therapists • Sensory-based input and techniques	• Mindfulness-based cognitive therapy • Dialectical behavior therapy (DBT) • Acceptance and commitment therapy (ACT) • Self-monitoring, role-playing	• Relaxation techniques to lower arousal • Exercises to stimulate arousal • Using music or other sensory input for changing arousal

Table 3.2. Essential theories that support development of How to Surf the Waves

How to Surf the Waves is based on existing theories that address the needs of children experiencing sensory, emotional, and behavioral dysregulation. This curriculum arises from both academic study and clinical experience with children. It sees the importance of shifting mindsets and guiding theories for certain children, depending on the specific individual and situation.

Theory Jumping

Knowing when to *theory jump*, or move from one theoretical foundation to another, can make the difference between finding an effective strategy, supports, or successful problem-solving and getting stuck in a pattern of ineffective techniques that fail to improve a situation or even reinforce or increase dysregulation and concerning behaviors or emotional states. This is more challenging than it sounds, especially for professionals who spend years studying why and how their profession's theory is the best and most effective. This is an understandable consequence of becoming well-versed in one approach, as it is essential that a professional understand and believe in the theoretical basis of what they are doing. The problem arises when strategies based on a particular theory *should* work to help support a child but ultimately *do not* work for a specific child or group of children. At this point, intervention can stagnate, and it is critical to know other approaches or theoretical constructs from which to pull alternative intervention approaches.

The theories in Table 3.2 are three of the more common theories used by professionals when working with children with sensory, emotional, and behavioral dysregulation. Additionally, many current theories and intervention strategies are derived from the grounding work of these theories.

It should be noted that *How to Surf the Waves* does not use behaviorism as a grounding theory. No tools, strategies, or activities in the curriculum are derived from behaviorism. Behavior is discussed only in the context of having children understand and consider how they feel about their own behavior.

CHAPTER FOUR

Strategies: How to Surf

How Do We Go from Theory to Effective Strategy?

If theories are the recipes and blueprints, effective strategies are the good ingredients and materials we need to create a support plan for a child. While moving away from the pathology and medical mindset for sensory, emotional, and behavioral dysregulation, it remains important to provide effective strategies for supporting and assisting children in the development of these skills and to provide the co-regulation and tools they need to regulate and feel less distress. Theories help determine what strategies will be effective in given situations.

The strategies and tools included in *How to Surf the Waves* focus on a variety of current sensory and cognitive-behavioral strategies in a neurodiversity-affirming manner for better access and efficacy. This does not negate emerging and/or effective tools and strategies based on other theories. They are simply not included as part of this curriculum as they are not specific to this author's area of academic study and clinical expertise. The following section includes descriptions of some of the strategies, derived from theories, that are used in *How to Surf the Waves*.

Sensory Strategies

Sensory strategies, including the use of various types of sensory input to stimulate or calm the nervous system, are included in each *How to Surf the Waves* unit because they provide effective and powerful techniques for children with sensory, emotional, and behavioral dysregulation. Sensory strategies can be used to help a child regulate a dysregulated nervous system, especially when the child is overwhelmed and unable to access their cognitive skills. Sensory strategies use the bottom-up approach to regulate the brain and nervous system, and they often provide a playful distraction to the child (*See Figure 2.2*).

The eight senses include not only the basic five senses, but also vestibular, proprioception, and interoception. Interoception has recently been recognized as the eighth sensory system. Kelly Mahler, OTD, OTR, initially brought interoception to prominence on the global stage, developing and expanding the concept. Information about interoception has been vital in helping people understand the importance of their internal body sensations. With better awareness of internal body sensations, students are more able to understand what they are feeling and why. Internal body sensations can unknowingly lead to emotional and behavioral dysregulation (Mahler, 2015).

It is noteworthy that while sensory strategies seem simple to understand and implement, the effect of sensory input on the nervous system is not always that clear. It is always ideal, whenever possible, to consult with an occupational therapist that is specifically trained in sensory integration prior to choosing the best supports for a child. The main issue to be concerned about is that the tool or strategy a person may think will help regulate a child because they are "seeking it out" may actually be dysregulating them. Looking for the subtle signs or knowing how and when to change to sensory input to be more regulating for a child takes education and practice. It requires tuning into the child and paying attention to non-verbal cues, vocalizations, reactions, and other expressions (*See Table 4.1*).

The Eight Sensory Systems Defined	
Auditory	*Hearing, sound, ears:* Information we hear or receive through the ears and auditory system, such as sound. Processed in the auditory cortex, which situated in the temporal lobe of the brain, where it is analyzed and translated into auditory perceptions, such as speech, music, and environmental sounds.
Visual	*Vision, eyes:* Information seen or received through our eyes and visual system, including shape, size, color, motion. Processed in the occipital lobe with interaction between the temporal and parietal lobes, which makes sense of and retains the visual information received.
Tactile	*Touch information, skin receptors:* Information received through the sense of touch. Processed by specialized receptors in the skin throughout the body and transmitted to the somatosensory cortex in the brain for interpretation and response. Involves the detection and interpretation of physical sensations on the skin (pressure, texture, temperature, and pain). Helps us perceive and understand object properties, textures, different levels of pressure, and navigate through our surroundings.
Gustatory	*Taste, mouth:* Information from taste buds located on the tongue, as well as in other areas of the oral cavity and throat. Processed in the gustatory cortex in the brain. Allows us to detect and discriminate between the five primary tastes: sweet, sour, salty, bitter, and umami (savory).
Olfactory	*Smell, nose:* Information from olfactory receptors in the nose detect airborne chemical molecules. Signals are transmitted to the brain for processing in the olfactory bulb at the base of the brain, then to the olfactory cortex. Connected with other areas of the brain, including the amygdala and hippocampus, hence the connection between smell and memory.
Proprioceptive	*Position and movement of body; muscles, joints, tendons:* Information from receptors located in muscles, tendons, and joints related to the position, movement, and spatial orientation of body parts. Provides a sense of where our body is in space and how it is moving, without relying on visual cues. Processed in various regions of the brain, including: primary somatosensory cortex, posterior parietal cortex, and cerebellum.
Vestibular	*Movement, inner ear:* Information from the vestibular system in the inner ear structures that detects changes in head position and motion. Helps with balance, perception of body position in space, and coordination of movement in response to vestibular input. Processed in the brainstem, vestibular nuclei, cerebellum, and parietal cortex.
Interoceptive	*Sensations inside the body, internal organs:* Information from internal state of the body, including heart rate, respiration, hunger, thirst, and emotions. Involves perceiving and interpreting internal bodily signals. Processed in various regions of the brain, including the insula, anterior cingulate cortex, and somatosensory cortex.

From https://sensoryhealth.org/basic/your-8-senses

Table 4.1. Definitions of the eight sensory systems

When choosing sensory strategies for a child, it is important to have detailed and accurate information about their individual nervous system and their preferences, aversions, and sensitivities. Sensory strategies can be presented to a child but should never be forced on them. It is also vital for those using sensory strategies to understand that there is no cookie cutter approach to delivering a one-size-fits-all sensory approach. Needs vary from moment to moment and can vastly differ between students. What one student enjoys or seeks out to help them regulate may be aversive or dysregulating for another. Therefore, consulting with those who know the regulation triggers and tools of preferences and benefit for a student is always best. Sensory strategies can address any or all of the eight sensory systems. Examples of strategies for the eight sensory systems are:

Auditory: Strategies for auditory input can include providing opportunities to increase sound/hearing or to minimize it. Some examples of auditory sensory strategies are: noise-canceling headphones to decrease background noise or volume, listening to calming music (60 beats/minute), white noise to help with background noise, Tibetan bowl or chimes, music of choice to help with mood and distraction, dance or rock music. It is noteworthy that while most consider slow, steady, soft, or mellow music and sound to be calming, many students are more regulated by intense, hard, or fast music and sound, which are typically more excitatory or stimulating. Again, it is always dependent on the individual nervous system response.

Visual: Visual sensory strategies include the aspects of light and darkness and the things we see or watch with our eyes. Typically, bright, flashing, florescent, or excessive light is considered stimulating or excitatory, while dim, muted, soft, or steady lights are thought to be calming. Other visual sensory strategies can include: light-up or spinning toys, car wheels that spin, race tracks, train tracks, sand toys, toys with falling or spilling (sand from hand into bin, water through funnel, color-changing toys, flashlights). For minimizing visual sensory input, strategies can include a clutter-free work area, few visual distractions, wearing sunglasses outside and inside.

Tactile/touch: Options for tactile sensory strategies can include: texture, pressure, or temperature. Input that is received in the tactile system comes through the skin. Some examples include: use of various tactile mediums or substances, such as playdough, slime, goo, sand, putty, moon sand, kinetic sand, shaving cream, lotion, beans, rice, finger paint, or items such as pops-its, stress balls, squishy toys, water tubes, stuffed animals or soft plush toys, and fabric.

Different elements of tactile input are important to consider for regulation, including: dry (chalk, sand, flour) or wet (water, lotion, shaving cream), sticky, slimy, or mushy items; hot (heated blankets/ warm clothes) and cold (ice packs, cold rags, cold water). Clothing textures and sensations are often important aspects of tactile sensory strategies, as they provide the closest input to the skin and provide continued sensory input to the body. Additionally, the hands and feet are two of the most sensitive areas of the body due to the higher concentration of sensory receptors. This makes sensory input into the hands and feet quite powerful for regulation.

Oral sensory—gustatory/taste: Gustatory strategies are derived from input into the taste receptors in the taste buds of the tongue and soft palate. These receptors are specialized and typically more sensitive than other sensory receptors. Tastes can be categorized into sweet, bitter, umami, as well as factors like salty, sour, and spicy. Taste options can be provided as sensory strategies and are highly effective for many students.

However, others can be extremely limited in their tolerance for tastes. Food, eating, and tasting can prompt a great deal of anxiety and distress for some students. Taste tools can include a mix of food items that offer opportunities for preferred or regulating taste, as tolerated. Consideration of the oral motor aspects of the item to taste is important, as well. Some examples include: pretzels or chips for salty, fruits for sweet and sour, vegetables for bitter, salty, sweet, etc. Typically, sour and spicy foods tend to be stimulating, but some students that require more input find these to be beneficial regulation tools.

Oral sensory—oral sensory input strategies: Oral sensory input is the phrase often used to talk about sensory input into the mouth or oral cavity. This is because the mouth includes a variety of sensory receptors including taste/gustatory receptors and somatosensory receptors that are proprioceptive, as well as tactile receptors that sense pain and temperature, while taste, touch, and proprioception are separate sensory systems (Chamoun et al., 2018). Oral sensory strategies can include taste, but also activities and sensations that impact the tactile receptors and proprioceptors in the mouth, including: tools and toys for blowing (whistles, pinwheels, or sucking from a straw), chewy tubes or safe non-food items to chew on, crunchy and/or chewy foods, and hot or cold food or drink items.

Olfactory/smell: Olfactory or smell sensory strategies include both exposure to smells or minimizing or removing noxious smells. When using exposure to smells as a strategy, it is best when scents are derived from natural sources rather than synthetic scents. It is important to remember that what we smell goes directly into our airways and lungs. When providing opportunities for increased olfactory input, smells such as lavender and vanilla are typically considered calming scents while mint or orange are thought to be more alerting, but individual preferences matter most. Limit or avoid perfumes and colognes, air fresheners, strong cleaners, scented fabric softeners, etc. whenever possible, especially if the child is not yet able to clearly indicate preference and aversions.

Proprioceptive: Proprioceptive input is also referred to as heavy work, and includes input into muscles, joints, and tendons. It helps with body position and movement. It is an especially powerful tool for regulation that can be easily and affordably provided for students in a variety of settings. Some examples of proprioceptive strategies include: deep pressure; weighted items (blankets, vests, lap pads); pushing, pulling, or carrying heavy items (backpacks loaded with books, heavy laundry baskets, or small hand weights); weight-bearing postures like yoga poses or lying prone (on stomach) propped on elbows; crashing into cushions, balls, bean bags; jumping; climbing a ladder or pole; walking on tiptoes; isometric exercises; and exercise band activities.

Vestibular: Vestibular strategies are focused on movement. Many movement activities also give opportunities for proprioceptive input. Some examples of primary vestibular input include: walking, running, swinging, spinning, skipping; or use of rocking chairs, ball chairs, slides, gliders, scooters, and bicycles/tricycles. Vestibular input can be very powerful, especially rotation, such as spinning. WARNING: Not everyone tolerates spinning. It can make some people feel quite ill, including vomiting. Please consult with a trained occupational therapist before implementing spinning and get recommendations regarding its safe use.

Interoception: Interoception strategies help increase a student's ability to tune in to their body and how it feels. Strategies used will vary based on age or stage and learning style. Some examples of interoceptive strategies include: body scans, check-ins, and mindfulness activities. Remember to use language that is appropriate for the child's level of receptive language abilities and offers adaptive opportunities to communicate understanding.

Health and Wellness Strategies

Health and wellness strategies are incorporated into the *How to Surf the Waves* curriculum and include: getting enough sleep, eating a balanced diet, limiting sugar, and getting enough exercise. While caregivers maintain the primary responsibility for health and wellness in a child's life, education and the promotion of health and wellness are included in the program, as these are particularly important for sensory, emotional, and behavioral regulation. For example, children who do not get adequate sleep will be limited in their energy reserves, which negatively impacts coping capacity when facing the challenges of daily life.

There is a great deal of evidentiary support to promote regular exercise as an important component of any health and wellness program, especially for those with difficulty managing emotions and behavior (Davison et al., 2016; Nicholson et al., 2011; Oriel et al., 2011; Sowa & Meulenbroek, 2012). Exercise is easily assimilated into a child's day during recess and physical education classes. In addition to the health and cardiac benefits, it provides significant amounts of sensory input, including vestibular and proprioceptive input.

Food, whether because of frequency, quantity, or content, has a significant impact on the brain and body. A hungry child will not be in an optimal place to handle stressors and challenges of the day. Some children require more consistent and frequent snacks or drinks to function at their best, based on unique metabolism rates. Some children can be behaviorally responsive to certain foods or additives, such as sugar and food dyes. Additionally, children with avoidant or restrictive food intake, which is especially common in neurodivergent children, are limited in their capacity to consume a healthy variety of foods by intense levels of distress and dysregulation arising from eating many foods.

While diet and nutrition are personal matters for families and medical professionals to manage, the impact of diet is frequently seen across all settings. Communication with caregivers is encouraged to work towards a team approach for helping students address these challenges. Whenever possible, non-judgmentally support parents in securing assistance from professionals to manage diet and nutritional needs for the child. Nutritionists can offer plenty of information and guidance.

If your child or student has avoidant/restrictive food intake stemming from sensory difficulties, and you believe that the situation is adversely affecting their health and nutrition, please consult with a qualified occupational therapist, nutritionist, or doctor to assess for sensory issues that may benefit from intervention. It is important to understand that children with avoidant or restrictive food intake are highly anxious when faced with consuming foods that are not preferred and using an approach that is too aggressive can intensify their discomfort.

Cognitive Strategies

Cognitive strategies play a foundational role in the *How to Surf the Waves* curriculum. They rely on cognitive processes as a basis for children to explore their body and brain feelings and tools to help regulate these feelings. The cognitive concepts presented in the program teach children, via age-appropriate and interesting terminology, about the importance of their body feelings, emotions, thoughts, and associated behaviors. Teaching children cognitive strategies empowers those who may feel powerless over their body and brain feelings to believe they can create meaningful change for themselves.

Some examples of cognitive strategies used in the *How to Surf the Waves* curriculum include:

- Self-monitoring
- Rating scales for emotions
- Self-talk
- Affirmations
- Use of logic and problem-solving
- Examining fears and thoughts for facts versus fiction
- Distraction
- Mindfulness (cognitive and sensory)
- Breathing exercises (cognitive and sensory)

Cognitive strategies in the curriculum do not attempt to cognitively appeal to a child to "calm down" or change their behavior with punitive consequences and rewards. Many professionals rely on asking a child to change their behavior to meet expectations, but while this is sometimes effective, how is this helping the child learn to understand and manage their sensory, emotional, and behavioral dysregulation? For example, telling a child that their behavior is not acceptable and that they are risking consequences and loss of privilege does not build relationships. It does not foster the growth and skills development for the child or provide skills for self-regulation and management. And it almost never works for some children.

When using a more collaborative and relationship-based approach, a professional can effectively use compassion and empathy to help teach the same cognitive skills, such as self-monitoring and understanding of natural consequences to create change. For example, "If you don't finish your class work now, then you may have less free time at home tonight. I am concerned that may make you sad. What do you think we should do? Is there any way I can help make this easier for you right now?" It is also important to remember that when some children are facing very large waves, they cannot benefit from this strategy. Recognizing when to switch to another tool is critical in helping them surf their waves.

One of the greatest mistakes a professional or caregiver can make in helping a student navigate their waves is to change expectations or routine without warning. Even if a professional believes that a student *should* be able to handle the changes, no matter how minute, these inconsistencies can have considerable consequences in terms of emotional reactions and behaviors. Working to increase flexibility is important, but knowing when and how to increase this for students that struggle with emotional and behavioral challenges is critical for not *creating* more, or even bigger, waves during their daily life.

When a child is in a significantly heightened state of distress, verbal communication and cognitive behavioral strategies can potentially heighten their distress. This is due to the inability of the brain to access cortical (thinking brain) reasoning skills in times of extreme distress or upset. When a child is emotionally dysregulated, they will often act as if they do not care about the consequences; this is typically because they are not fully able to process the situation. It is best to discuss consequences of negative behaviors *prior* to the waves occurring. Boundaries and consequences should be consistent and clear ahead of time to prevent tsunamis.

Narrative Therapy

Narrative therapy is a psychological treatment model that moves away from the idea of deficits and dysfunction, instead using the child's skills to help them get through difficult times by emphasizing capabilities, developing confidence, and personal empowerment (Baldwin, 2020). Narrative therapy can also be beneficial for helping people navigate challenging situations and transitions in life (Lau-Zhu & Mann, 2023). This therapy is non-blaming, non-judgmental, and looks at the child as the expert about their experience. It is a beneficial approach for changing the narrative from a "bad kid" or "problem child" to that of a child whose experiences and actions may be sometimes be problematic but are not personality or character traits. As with most treatment models, there are many strategies and techniques that can be used as part of narrative therapy. Some examples of narrative therapy techniques include:

- Writing one's story, storytelling

- Drawing situations or places of difficulty and brainstorming solutions or coping strategies

- Positive self-talk or affirmations

- Creating external tools, such as worry jars or toolboxes for ADHD or sensory issues

- Calm and safe place drawings or stories

- Superhero metaphor

Surf Stories

Surf Stories is a cognitive strategy developed for the *How to Surf the Waves* program. In addition to familiar cognitive strategies, *Surf Stories*, which are derived from both narrative therapy and cognitive therapies, were developed for the *How to Surf the Waves* program. *Surf Stories* are described below, along with examples.

Creating *Surf Stories*:

Although the *Surf Stories* strategy was developed specifically for this program, it can be used and applied across various settings and contexts. *Surf Stories* are a tool that helps students better understand and predict situations, then plan out what tools or supports may be needed. They provide information on what to expect ahead of time to help decrease feelings of uncertainty and self-judgment. A *Surf Story* is meant to be individualized, non-judgmental, and not be used to direct or change behavior. The *Surf Story* is about how a person feels in their own brain and body. It is not about how they should feel, how everyone else feels, or how to act as if they feel a certain way.

Social experiences, for example, cannot be separated from sensory experiences and needs. Simply teaching a student the words to say in a social setting will not prevent the student from sensory experiences that are internal or inherent in the setting or activity. A *Surf Story* is about the things one must do to cope with situations that are highly dysregulating. When writing a *Surf Story*, the focus is on self-experience and taking care of one's self rather than the impact of what we are doing with or around another person, which can cause masking.

A *Surf Story* is prepared ahead of time and can be read and rehearsed repeatedly to help a person stay safe and grounded. This can include self-affirmations, suggested tools, and reminders. For example, for a person required to attend a crowded event in a large auditorium, such as an assembly or concert, the experience can be very overwhelming from a sensory perspective (*See Sample 1*).

School Assembly Surf Story (Sample 1)

Next week I will go to an assembly at my school. All the students in the school will be there. It is going to be very crowded with people moving all around when coming in and out of the room and moving in their seats.

There will be bright lights, then low lights when the assembly starts, then possibly spotlights or changing lights. All of this may bother my eyes or make me feel distracted and confused.
- *I can always close my eyes and take some time to reset if I feel this way.*
- *I can remind myself that I am safe and have been to assemblies before and am always OK.*
- *I can bring my fidget toy/tool with me and use that to help me feel better.*

It will also be very noisy when students are coming in and out of the auditorium. Then it may get very quiet before music or voices will come on the speakers, which may really bother my ears.
- *I can bring my noise-reducing headphones in case it gets too loud.*
- *I may need to rock a little in my seat or move my hands in a way that helps me feel better if it gets too uncomfortable. That is OK because this is how my body helps my brain feel better.*

It is also possible that I will smell odors from people that are really uncomfortable for me.
- *I can always put my sleeve to my nose and smell my clothes, or I can bring something I like the smell of (lip balm or something else) in case the smells get too overwhelming and I need to smell something else.*

When I am sitting in the close-together chairs and people are moving in and out of the auditorium, I may get bumped or accidentally touched. Even though the person may not mean to bump or touch me, it will still really bother me and that's OK.
- *I will do my best to cope with how I feel.*
- *I can do some breathing exercises or squeeze my hands closed tightly, which gives me the pressure I need.*
- *If I need help with any of these, I can ask my lifeguard for help.*
- *I can ask to sit at the end of a row in case I need a break. If it is too much, I can ask to leave.*

The overwhelming sensory input can trigger intense distress and emotions such as fear, irritability, agitation, and more. An adult can interview the student following one such event or in advance of an upcoming situation. The adult asks the child questions about their brain and body feelings and what helps them feel better. A *Surf Story* should be written by the student with adult assistance and provided to instructors, parents, and other people who provide support to the student.

Another way to individualize and increase the impact of a *Surf Story* is to include special interests, such as characters, animals, or facts that are important to the child, as shown below in the *Surf Story* Sample 2.

School Assembly Surf Story (Sample 2)

Sometimes when I have to go to an assembly, I feel big waves of feelings. It is hard for me to sit still and focus when there are so many people close to me and so much noise. The lights are bright, and everything can be distracting.

I really like dinosaurs and my brain and body feel better when I am thinking about or looking at dinosaurs. I will take my favorite dinosaur book or toy to the assembly, and this will help my brain and body when I am having a hard time. I can think about the names of all my favorite dinosaurs and remember what they like to eat. This can help me feel better.

Many students experience distress from the noise and movement caused by fire drills. *Surf Story* Sample 3 can help students prepare and practice using their tools for the next fire drill.

Fire Drill at School Surf Story (Sample 3)

The fire alarm in my school is very loud and it hurts my ears and scares me a lot. I am not the only one who feels this way, but it may hurt my ears more than it hurts others' so I may need more help with this and that is OK.

I know it has to be loud to get people's attention, but I still get very upset when we have fire drills. I cannot get away from the sound, but I can use my surfboard tools to help me cope with how I feel and get through the fire drill safely.

- *I need to tell my lifeguards how hard this is. We can work together to help me stay safe and feel OK.*
- *I am allowed to put on my noise-reducing headphones, which can help.*
- *Sometimes I also put my hands or fingers to my ears to hold them closed and make the noise not as loud.*
- *I will use my breathing exercises to help me feel better as I am leaving the building and the noise is still happening.*
- *I can also open and close my hands tightly and quickly—I can even count how many times I can open and close them before I get outside. This will help my brain and body feel better.*
- *Sometimes I press my lips together tightly or squeeze my hands together to help my body feel better again.*

For students fearful about going to an appointment, such as the dentist, *Surf Story* Sample 4 provides a script that provides strategies for a successful experience.

> ### *Going to the Dentist Surf Story* (Sample 4)
>
> *I am going to the dentist this week. I may feel a little nervous or scared. It is OK to feel nervous or scared when I go to the dentist, and many people feel this way. The dentist is important for my health so I will use all the tools I need to help me get through the visit and feel safe.*
>
> *I don't like the sound of the dentist.*
> - *I will wear my headphones and listen to music, or I will watch my favorite YouTube video.*
> - *I feel better when I have a fidget tool in my hand so I will take my fidgets in the room with me.*
> - *If I feel scared when I am in there, that is OK. I will use my breathing tools to help me surf the waves of my feelings. The feelings will pass.*
> - *I can ask for help if I need it, and I will remember that I am loved and safe.*

Dialectical Behavioral Therapy Strategies

Some cognitive strategies in *How to Surf the Waves* are derived from Dialectical Behavior Therapy (DBT). DBT involves looking at helpful versus unhelpful ways to deal with unpleasant feelings. DBT is a specific type of cognitive behavior therapy that originated through the work of psychologist Marsh Linehan in the 1980s. The word *dialectical* is used to describe the integration of two opposites—acceptance and change. For example, a person may be encouraged to accept their feelings and simultaneously be non-judgmentally encouraged and supported to change their thoughts and behaviors (Garey, 2022). Some examples of DBT include:

- **Mindfulness:** being present and aware in the moment

- **Distress tolerance:** withstanding discomfort or distress in different situations

- **Interpersonal effectiveness:** how to interact more effectively and feel better supported by others while maintaining self-respect

- **Emotion regulation:** managing, responding effectively to emotional situations and changing emotions

It is important to note that some DBT practices and skills are not neurodiversity-affirming. The elements of DBT included in this curriculum have been adapted for use with children who need support with managing intense emotions and regulation, in order to support and develop their skills while accepting that they are currently doing the best they can. Of particular benefit are the DBT concepts of distress tolerance and self-soothing. These distress tolerance skills are also helpful in teaching older children how to manage sensory sensitivities and distress in their environments when they are unable to completely control their exposure to sensory stimuli. As with any therapeutic intervention, it is important to consult a skilled and credentialed therapist for proper assessment and evaluation.

Mindfulness as a Strategy

Mindfulness is becoming increasingly popular. Mindfulness has several different meanings and applications. First, it is the psychological state of being fully aware in the present moment. Mindfulness meditation, in which individuals meditate to focus the mind on being fully aware in the present moment, has its roots in Buddhism. In the 1970s, professor Jon Kabat-Zinn took the concept of mindfulness meditation, and by filtering out the more religious and philosophical components, created a modified version. Kabat-Zinn created what is currently known as mindfulness-based stress reduction, which incorporates mindfulness meditation, yoga, and body awareness (Goldin & Gross, 2010).

Mindfulness-Based Intervention (MBI) refers to a structured approach or program that incorporates mindfulness practices and principles to promote well-being, reduce distress, and address specific psychological or physical conditions. MBI is frequently adapted to target specific populations or areas of concern. *How to Surf the Waves* includes multiple aspects of MBI—from yoga and body awareness to specific mindfulness and cognitive activities designed to promote self-awareness, sensory, and emotional regulation, and overall well-being. These activities teach children skills such as connecting with their body, mindful breathing, focused attention, and mindful listening. These skills help children learn how to become aware and focused on the moment, instead of thinking about the past or future. They also teach children positive coping skills for preventing and managing episodes of distress and dysregulation. An increasing body of research supports the benefits of MBI for children, such as improved self-control, decreased emotional reactivity, improved mental flexibility, improved focus, and reduced stress (Amundsenet al., 2020; Felver et al., 2016; Flook et al., 2010; Schonert-Reichl et al., 2015).

Yoga as a Strategy

Yoga is also included in *How to Surf the Waves* because it combines both sensory strategies (proprioceptive input—movement stretch and weight-bearing input to the child's muscles, joints, and tendons) and cognitive strategies (slow deep breathing and relaxation skills). Yoga can also help children improve body awareness, manage stress, and build concentration. Through the incorporation of slow and controlled movements, combined with deep breathing, the parasympathetic nervous system is activated, which is responsible for the body's relaxation response (Kamraju, 2023; Kiecolt-Glaser et al., 2010).

How to Use the Curriculum: Becoming a Surfing Instructor

The *How to Surf the Waves* curriculum provides a structured set of instructional activities organized into five units. Through detailed explanations and instructions, facilitators will be equipped to help students understand and use the surfing analogy, master the basic concepts, then learn how to apply these concepts to their own lives.

What Are the Components of the Five Units?

Each unit is built around a specific concept, but it is up to the instructor to choose the activities that match the interests and abilities of the students. Not all activities will work for all students, depending on learning style, interest level, and motivation. It is important to present the program in a differentiated manner to ensure content is accessible to all students. We recommend you present the activities in order, regardless of which ones you select, as the topics build across the units. Each of the *Surfing* units has a consistent set of components:

- **Introduction and Objectives**—Each unit starts with an introduction explaining the core idea. This is followed by the objectives. Read and become familiar with the introduction and objectives before beginning the unit activities. It may be helpful to review the objectives with the students prior to starting.

- **Yoga Activity**—Yoga is an evidenced-based self-regulation technique. Each unit provides poses that incorporate the whole body and help regulate the nervous system for participation. The yoga poses provided are easily adapted and can be used with different ages across a variety of settings. For individuals with physical limitations due to age or disability, you may omit the part of poses that include balance, e.g., rather than balancing on one foot, a child may stand on both feet, or if a child is unable to raise their arms above their head, it's fine to have them hold their arms at shoulder height. Use the yoga poses as an opening activity, repeating the poses at the start of each session for that unit to support familiarity and mastery.

Note: It is important to note that some individuals have religious and/or other cultural objections to yoga. These objections should be respected. Exercises that incorporate the same components can be used instead.

- ***Wave Watch* Check-In**—Units 2-5 include a check-in with the *Wave Watch*. (Note: For more information about the *Wave Watch*, see Chapter 6.) Have students indicate their feelings at that moment by selecting a wave (calm water, small, medium, large, tsunami) or corresponding number before beginning the cognitive activities. Explore why students choose a certain wave, especially if they choose the same wave every time. You can share examples of how your own waves change from day to day. If you feel the child is not grasping the *Wave Watch*, as their own perception does not match your observations, tell them what you are seeing or hearing (e.g., "You are talking loud and fast and you are moving around a lot. You seem full of energy."). You can use the *Wave Watch* at the start and end of each lesson to help students identify changes in their waves after doing activities.

- **Cognitive Concepts**—Each unit contains a number of cognitive activities: exploring and identifying feelings and tools, rating intensity of feelings, problem-solving, affirmations, and more. These activities are designed to provide students with a chance to learn about themselves, identify their body and brain feelings, and problem-solve. Presenting these activities in a non-judgmental and encouraging way is an important component of the lessons.

  Students should not be made to perform components of activities that may in themselves trigger waves (e.g., reading, writing, or performing in front of a group). The instructor can adapt the presentation of the materials, e.g., read the directions and material aloud rather than having students read to themselves, allowing students to practice role-playing activities at their desks rather than in front of the class, etc. This allows students to focus on the content, rather than on skills such as reading or writing, and helps students approach the concepts with more confidence and engagement. Teach in the way that students learn best.

- **Sensory Activities**—A variety of sensory activities are included in each unit to help facilitate learning and promote active engagement. There are multiple activities that offer both tactile and visual input, such as exploration bins. There are also sensorimotor activities that offer movement and input into the muscles, joints, and tendons. Interoception activities are included to help students begin to understand and describe how their internal body sensations are feeling. Additionally, there are supplemental sensory activity suggestions provided that can be worked into the units or used at other times. Activities are labeled as Sensory Motor, Sensory Tactile, and Sensory Visual Motor.

- **Mindfulness**—Each teaching session should end with a mindfulness activity. The inclusion of mindfulness activities at the end of every unit is meant to both introduce and explore mindfulness skills and to provide a regulating ending activity. The mindfulness activities include mindful breathing and mindful listening, and other activities meant to encourage each student to notice and focus on their body and environment differently. Mindfulness is meant to be continually practiced, so doing the same mindfulness activity for each session of the unit will better teach and enhance the skills.

- **Resources**—Links to videos, pictures, and websites are at the end of each unit. Please refer to the resources for additional support with specific cognitive concepts and activities.

How Do I Teach the Surfing Units?

Each unit has five topics. Each topic contains cognitive and sensory activities that can be used across as few as five or as many as ten lessons, depending on the schedule and student needs. To design a lesson or therapy session, consider the topic and select specific activities to meet the students' level of interest and ability.

Each unit relies on adult instruction and support, both in providing the initial information and in completing all activities and handouts. Handouts should not be used in isolation, but should instead be used to support mastery of the concepts. Instructors should proceed through each unit in order, teaching the concepts through the guided activities. Lessons can be presented in 30- to 50-minute blocks or in multiple shorter sessions.

Lessons are designed to build on the unit concepts, starting with the beginning concepts in Unit 1 and ending with the more complex concepts in Unit 5. When planning a lesson, consider the following:

- Start each lesson with a yoga pose, then teach one or more cognitive concepts and/or sensory activities, and end with a mindfulness activity.

- Choose those activities most appropriate for the student's age, interest, and motivation. While it is ideal to use all unit activities, sometimes lesson time constraints or specific child needs do not permit the use of all activities.

- Plan a set of activities that can be completed during the lesson time block.

- Structure lessons so that cognitive activities are sandwiched between yoga or movement/stretch activities at the beginning and mindfulness or calming activities at the end.

- Provide learning supports, accommodations, and modifications to ensure each student is successful.

How Do I Adapt Activities to Meet the Needs of All Students?

Basic adaptations—It is important to provide appropriate accommodations and modifications for the unique learning and sensory needs of each student. Examples for providing these supports are:

- Adjust to a student's learning style, including visual, auditory, multisensory, or kinesthetic.

- If students cannot process the language for the cognitive tasks due to age, ability, or lack of engagement/inattention, they can still participate in the sensory activities for that unit and topic. The instructor can also adjust activities to meet the needs of specific students.

- Use simple visuals or videos to identify emotions. Happy and sad are a good starting place for self-monitoring of emotional states. For example, if a student is in distress, show the "sad" visual or video and say something like, "You seem sad. Your body and face look like the picture." This can be used with any emotion and sends the message, "I see you are uncomfortable and I am here to help."

- For self-monitoring of emotional states, provide visual reminders or info sheets, such as the *Wave Watch*, around the classroom (posted on the wall or in work areas) and for students to carry in their notebooks or backpacks.

- Offer options for students who struggle academically or emotionally with academic tasks, especially with writing or spelling. For example,
  - Allow students to produce their work in a variety of mediums, including on paper, on a whiteboard (vertical or flat), verbally, or on the computer.
  - Offer choices for students to provide answers in alternative ways, including using an augmentative and alternative communication (AAC) device, or pointing to visuals, objects, photos, or pictures.
- For non-readers, younger students, or those with language processing communication differences, provide concrete examples and use visuals, AAC devices, and other support tools to present the concepts.
- Allow students to engage in movement and other sensory activities when presenting cognitive concepts rather than have them seated for table-top presentations. Choose a task or input that is known to be calming or rewarding for each student.
- Be aware that students can be attending even if they are not looking, so accept limited eye contact, checking for understanding before moving on to the next concept.
- In your role as facilitator, begin to recognize the students' triggers and typical wave patterns to help them label their feelings and emotions.

Special interests—Special interests are when someone has an intense focus on specific topics. This trait is commonly observed in autistic children and other neurodivergent individuals, but it can also be found in neurotypical children. Special interests can range from items to topics and hobbies. They can be specific, such as a certain type of rock, a video game, a character, trains, otters, rainbows, etc., to broader categories like transportation, dinosaurs, books, letters, animals, and more. Children with special interests will often be highly motivated by incorporating specific interests into instructional activities across the curriculum. While special interests can sometimes be restrictive and repetitive, research supports the benefits of incorporating special interests for children, including mitigating anxiety and engaging in meaningful pursuits (Patten Koenig & Hough Williams, 2017).

Using special interests to increase engagement and enhance the impact of *How to Surf the Waves* is encouraged. For example, placing pictures of a child's special interest, (e.g., a flag, a train, or a dinosaur) on the *Wave Watch* may help increase engagement and improve the overall impact of the program. Special interests are sometimes more general but can be incorporated into other aspects of the program or lessons.

Incorporating art—Art may be a preferred or engaging method for increasing student participation and overall outcomes. Some examples of art activities include:

- Locate pictures that support various lesson activities in print materials, such as magazines or online resources to make collages, posters, etc.
- Draw or paint different scenes depicting lesson concepts, based on ability level.
- Use playdough, model magic, clay, and other media to create objects from lessons, such as waves, surfboards, sharks, or anything you feel students are interested in.

Incorporating technology—Any lesson can be adapted to include a digital format. Enhance lesson activities and increase student interest and motivation with the following:

- Search the internet* for pictures and videos of real people related to surf themes, such as waves, surfers, lifeguards, sharks, or storms.

- Make a digital photo collage representing lesson concepts related to surfing themes, waves, emotions, feelings, or surfing tools.

- Find various sensory tools to copy and paste into a document that can be printed or accessed on a device for personal reference.

*Please view any internet videos first to ensure the content has not been altered and remains appropriate.

Adaptations based on age or abilities—Some students may resist anything that appears too childish, such as certain pictures or activities. Simple adaptations can be made to match the students' needs. Examples include:

- Ask older students to share their thoughts about things that would be interesting and motivating to increase their buy-in.

- Replace visuals that may seem too childish with high-interest pictures of similarly-aged students.

- Provide pictures from current media, including popular movie and game characters.

- Involve students in finding or creating visuals that are motivating and high-interest using various resources, including approved online websites.

- Include art activities using various mixed media and online resources.

How Do Instructors and Therapists Incorporate Academics or Address IEP Goals Within the Curriculum?

Notes for the Teacher

The activities in each unit can be incorporated into the classroom schedule throughout the day and can be used with the whole class, in small groups, or individually. Activities can be differentiated for those with low- to high-support needs and a range of cognitive abilities. It is important to make sure the demands of the activities are aligned with the students' skills to avoid increasing frustration and dysregulation. For example, if a student has dysgraphia or is very avoidant of paper-and-pencil tasks, use the activity sheets as a visual and structural guide for verbal discussion and to document answers, responses, and information for the student, via dictation if needed, in order to permit a focus on hands-on activities.

The *How to Surf the Waves* curriculum directly supports social emotional learning goals in areas of self- and social awareness, self-management, decision-making, and relationship skills. Teachers can also easily embed other educational goals and objectives from multiple academic content areas into many unit activities (e.g., reading, vocabulary, math, science, health, etc.). Additionally, learning goals for all content areas of the curriculum can be developed to be standards-aligned, varying with the state standards adopted by different states.

Notes for Therapists

These units and activities are designed for use among therapists of various disciplines. They are broken up into manageable segments to incorporate into group or individual sessions. Therapy goals or IEP goals can easily be addressed within each unit and lesson of the program. Examples of goal areas that can be addressed or paired with the curriculum are shown in Table 5.1.

Goal Areas for Therapy, Instruction, or the IEP	
Regulation: • Self-regulation • Co-regulation • Emotional regulation • Identifying emotions • Rating emotional intensity	*Sensory:* • Sensory processing • Sensory registration • Sensory modulation • Interoceptive awareness
Speech and Language: • Core vocabulary • Receptive and expressive language • Communicating feelings with words/symbols • Problem-solving • Figurative language • Neurodiverse-affirming pragmatics, two-way perspective taking	*Fine Motor/Visual Motor:* • Hand-eye coordination • Pencil grasp and pressure • Precision and control • Spatial awareness • Cutting skills • Mixing and measuring • Ocular motor skills • Graphomotor skills (color, draw, write) • Tool use
Neuromuscular and Gross Motor Skills: • Balance • Postural control and stability • Motor planning • Flexibility • Strength • Bilateral Coordination	*Self-Determination:* • Self-awareness • Self-advocacy • Increased engagement and participation in daily life • Body autonomy
Executive Function Skills: • Working memory • Inhibition/initiation • Planning/organization • Cognitive flexibility • Emotional control	• Goal setting • Self-monitoring • Sustained attention • Organization of materials

Table 5.1. Sample goals for therapy, instruction, or the IEP

How Do Instructors Support Generalization of the Concepts?

In addition to the suggestions within the curriculum, instructors can also have students build a *Regulation Binder*, in which they include completed worksheets or visual supports. This helps students keep information in a centralized place so that they can refer to materials throughout the day, serving to reinforce the concepts and encourage their use in everyday life.

CHAPTER SIX

Exploring the Topics: Testing the Waves

The curriculum portion of *How to Surf the Waves* is designed to meet the needs of a variety of student levels and needs. In order to teach the units effectively, it is important for instructors to be familiar with the information and rationale for each unit, as presented in this chapter.

Unit 1: Waves in Motion

In Unit 1, students will learn that waves represent the ups and downs of daily life, emotionally and physiologically. These include all the highest and lowest good and bad moments: from meltdowns and over-the-top hyperactivity to feeling mellow, calm, or happy. Everyone will wipe out on a wave from time to time. The goal is getting used to these inevitable falls—making it through the waves and getting back up on the board. Waves come in various sizes throughout the day, and the size of the wave a student has to surf can make or break their success with the situation.

Using the *Wave Watch*

The *Wave Watch* is a self-rating scale and an essential visual and teaching tool in the *How to Surf the Waves* curriculum. Self-rating scales provide a visual tool that allow children

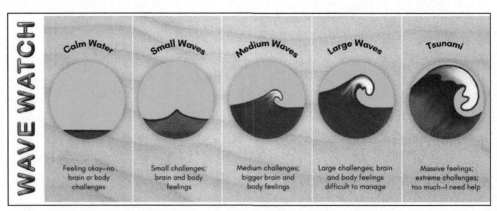

to understand that there are degrees of feelings. This helps children learn to identify the intensity of their feelings in different situations. There are several versions of the *Wave Watch* that also include numbers or emojis to support differentiation and effectiveness for different students *(See Unit 1, Topic 4.1)*.

When using the *Wave Watch*, it is helpful to read the descriptions of the different waves. Some students will benefit from the emojis and numbers in rating the intensity of their feelings. Once students understand that feelings come in different intensities, they can start to rate the intensity of their feelings in hypothetical and past situations. If the students are struggling with accuracy or awareness, instructors can provide feedback on what they have observed. Providing personal examples and acting out situations can also be beneficial. Once students have mastered this concept, they will be better able to use the rating scale to predict future feelings and waves. This awareness allows the students the opportunity to start planning for tools they can use to surf their waves.

Learning that stressors come in different sizes and intensities, and exploring what creates different waves, is the first step toward helping students surf the waves of daily life. Causes of waves, such as triggers or stressors, and the size of the waves will vary, as everyone is unique. Examples of types of waves:

Calm Water
No waves to surf. These are times when a student is in a calm and alert state, ready to work or play in the "just right" mindset and physical state.

Small Waves
These waves present minimal highs/lows and limited challenges and stress. They are often manageable with the right responses. Possible small waves include:

- Low mood or energy
- Non-preferred activities (class work)
- Transitions
- Mild excitement
- Small stressors

Medium Waves
These waves present a moderate risk. It is important to help students learn to work through these waves, or they risk wiping out as escalation occurs. Possible medium waves include:

- Moderate emotional states (e.g., frustration, anger, excitement)
- Homework
- Unexpected moderate-intensity sensory experiences (noises, touch, smells, etc.)
- Bus rides
- Transitions from preferred to non-preferred activities
- Unstructured activity time (lunch, recess)
- Games/sports with peers or siblings
- Small schedule changes

Large Waves

These are big waves and can be quite dangerous for surfers. They can be either positive or negative experiences or situations. Large waves cause stress and challenges for the surfer and often lead to meltdowns or extreme reactions and behaviors. Large waves can quickly become tsunamis. Possible large waves include:

- Strong emotional states

- Intense unexpected sensory experiences (noises, touch, smells, etc.)

- Loss of privilege, punishment

- Significant change in desired plans

- Arguments or conflict with others

- High-difficulty tasks

- Exposure to situations that cause distress or fear

Tsunami

This is a giant and dangerous wave that occurs when a student is in crisis and needs assistance for safety and personal wellness. A tsunami often follows right behind a large wave that was not navigated properly. Tsunamis can arise from challenges or smaller waves that involve intense emotional and arousal states and have not been appropriately managed. During a tsunami, a student will probably be unable to use their cognitive skills to talk, calm down, or be rational, as the severe and intense distress overrides all logical thought or reasoning. It is best to talk about what happened *after* the fact by helping a student identify what happened to them both before and during their tsunami, and helping them predict future tsunamis.

Unit 2: Surfing and Surfboards

One of the most important parts of surfing is having and maintaining a good surfboard. Unit 2 explains how surfboards represent the tools and strategies that help children surf the waves of daily life. These tools and strategies, which are unique to each student, can decrease the intensity and duration of waves. Some children need to use their body to self-regulate; some need to use their brain. All children are different and so are the tools they require.

Children are the best source of information about their needs, so it is important to involve students in the process of identifying what works for them and what does not. Many of the activities in this unit are designed to guide students through the process of identifying what works best for them.

Children will sometimes indicate a preference for tools that have the opposite effect from what you, as a facilitator, may want to see. In these moments, it is important to explain to the student what you are seeing. For example, if the student is sluggish, sad, or at a low arousal level, they may select a tool of going to sit in a beanbag chair to get them more alert. Although that may be an enjoyable or soothing tool, it may not be one that would increase their engagement and activity level. However, it should never be a matter of right or wrong choices, and students should not be told what works for them.

You can use situations as teachable moments by sharing your observations. For example, if a student picks fidget toys as a tool and you observe this increasing distractibility or impeding task behavior, use this opportunity to tell them what you see and why you do not think it is a good fit for a surfboard in the moment. For example, "What I see right now is that you are really enjoying playing with that toy and your eyes are not looking at your work, which will make it take longer for you to finish."

While the list of surfboard options is vast, some basic categories can be presented to students to help them identify the different strategies and tools available. The purpose of this lesson is to explore new tools that the student may not know are available and to identify what works and what does not. It is just as important for a student to identify and explore what they do not like as what they do like. If a student does not *want* or *agree* to use a tool, it will likely be ineffective. The following categories contain examples of useful surfboard tools.

Body Tools

Body tools are surfboard tools that help with regulation by showing students how to tune in to and support their physiological needs. Body tools are bottom-up tools that incorporate aspects of sensory strategies, environmental control, and awareness of general health and wellness. These tools are some of the most important surfboard strategies for ensuring that the day's waves stay calm and manageable. Exploring these tools can engage students to expand their understanding of what helps them surf their waves. Body tools can greatly influence changing arousal states and help students surf their waves more smoothly. These non-cognitive tools allow the student to change their state or mood and decrease or manage their daily stressors without having to think about it. Examples of body tools include:

- Environmental control: limited visual distractions on the walls, appropriate (non-distressing) lighting, limitation of background noise, using a soft and gentle voice

- Health and wellness tools: getting enough sleep, eating a balanced diet, limiting sugar, and getting enough exercise

- Sensory strategies of all kinds including:

  o Auditory (sound): music of various tempos and frequencies, soft or loud voices, background noises
  o Visual (eyes): dim or bright lights in the environment, sun or shade, visually-stimulating toys
  o Gustatory and oral sensory (taste and texture): foods of various textures and tastes, non-food oral items such as chew tubes, blowing bubbles, and whistles
  o Tactile (touch): textures and touch to skin, lotions/shaving cream, fidget toys, tolerable clothing, tactile mediums (sand, slime, putty, rice)
  o Olfactory (smell): use natural scents and limit bad or chemical scents or smells in the environment, including scents on people
  o Proprioceptive (input into muscles, joints, and tendons): deep pressure, crashing, squeezing, pushing, weighted blankets
  o Vestibular (movement): spinning, swinging, running, jumping, rocking
  o Interoception: sensations inside the body, internal organs (bladder/bowels), heart rate, breathing, cold, hot, pain, sickness

  Note: Many of these tools require adult support or assistance in procuring or setting up activities.

Brain Tools

Brain tools are surfboard tools that include cognitive strategies, coping skills and tools, and elements of mindfulness. These are top-down tools that require the use of cognitive processes to understand aspects of sensory and emotional regulation. For example, having a child use the *Wave Watch* to rate their waves prior to starting a task is a brain tool. Some other examples of brain tools include:

- Self-monitoring

- Rating scales for emotions

- Affirmations, self-talk

- Direct conversation and talking about a problem to help solve it

- Individual and neurodiversity-affirming *Surf Stories*

- Cognitive distraction techniques: storytelling, discussing their favorite game or subject

- Technology: YouTube, tablet/iPad, video games, computer, TV

- Reading or listening to a book

- Consistent structure and predictability in their daily schedule

- Assistive technology and the ability to type (as opposed to write) during school when a student is emotionally stressed by writing demands.

Unit 3: Finding Lifeguards

Unit 3 explains that lifeguards are the people in a student's life who help them surf their waves. Children need to identify people who can assist them while learning to navigate the ups and downs of daily life. Lifeguards are the co-regulators that help soothe and manage stressful situations so a child can remain or become regulated. Whether they need support in a particularly stressful moment, or they are in crisis and need a lifeguard to help get them back to a calm, safe, and functional place, learning to identify whom to seek out in these times is critical. This unit not only teaches students how to identify lifeguards in their lives, but also supports them in mastering the skill of requesting the help that they need.

One of the most important qualities for a lifeguard is to understand the root causes behind a student's sensory, emotional, and behavioral regulation difficulties. Adults should never assume that a child's struggles are willful or manipulative. If you are a professional working with students that experience dysregulation, it is critical to understand the underlying reasons for their challenges and to support their positive efforts. Instead of getting stuck in frustration and blame mode, instructors and other professionals have the power to create an environment in which students can thrive.

Examples of lifeguards include:
- Caregivers and/or family members
- Teachers/instructors
- Classroom aides
- Other school staff
- Therapists (Occupational Therapists, Speech-Language Therapists, mental health professionals)

- Siblings

- Peers

Caution! *Not all people in a child's life can be lifeguards! Being aware of a good fit is essential. Many instructors and professionals are not compatible with or do not have a good rapport with certain students. Finding this out the hard way can be stressful for everyone.*

Unit 4: Watch Out for Sharks

This unit teaches children what to watch out for when surfing the waves of daily life. These are more than just the waves; they are what makes surfing the waves harder and more dangerous. These challenges or triggers are described as sharks in the water. Students learn that sharks are part of life—situations or triggers they can prepare for.

Students will practice predicting the presence of sharks by noticing warning signs, getting help and support, and using their surfboard tools to out surf or avoid them. Using the shark analogy can also be beneficial in encouraging children to talk about their most worrisome problems or stressors without the pressure of being put on the spot. Identifying each student's shark situations is critical to helping them successfully surf their daily ups and downs.

Unit 5: Surviving the Storm

This final unit pulls together all of the concepts of *How to Surf the Waves*. The goal of the program is to teach children to understand the stressors, challenges, and triggers of daily life, and to learn skills to help them effectively navigate these challenges—to surf their waves. Surviving the Storm teaches students how to use their knowledge to problem-solve and minimize the impact of the waves in their daily life. The storm analogy is used in this unit because storms create new waves and make existing waves bigger. Storms, like stressors, are inevitable for everyone. Sometimes they are predictable but sometimes they come out of the blue. Just as we can predict a weather storm by looking for the signs (dark clouds, thunder), students can learn to predict their own emotional storms. This unit goes beyond identifying sharks (predicting triggers) and helps students create a plan and problem-solve for when the waves are inevitable. They can keep a small wave from becoming a tsunami.

An important component of *Surviving the Storm* is learning to predict waves. Predicting waves helps students understand the relationship of their various thoughts, emotions, arousal states, and experiences to their choices and behaviors. Engaging students in this process allows them to build self-monitoring and self-regulation skills, which are extremely important in surfing our waves.

For students who cannot independently perform self-monitoring and problem-solving due to age/stage, cognitive ability or other factors, the caregivers and professionals in their lives become integral to this step. Learning how to read cues, assess a child's mood or state, and identify potential triggers is an important part of managing and minimizing the frequency, duration, and intensity of behavioral and emotional distress.

PART TWO
HOW TO SURF THE WAVES CURRICULUM

UNIT 1: WAVES IN MOTION

INTRODUCTION

Unit 1 introduces students to the analogy of surfing the waves. Topics within this unit address waves, emotions, and feelings, and how these are connected.

- <u>Topic 1</u> is about how waves in the ocean sometimes feel incredibly big and overwhelming, or sometimes small and manageable.
- <u>Topic 2</u> describes and explains body feelings and senses.
- <u>Topic 3</u> describes and explains brain feelings and emotions, including different intensities.
- <u>Topic 4</u> helps students understand how feelings are like waves, and that they are caused by situations and emotions.
- <u>Topic 5</u> allows students to explore and compare their own emotions and feelings to wave sizes.

OBJECTIVES

Students will master the following concepts:

Topic 1: What Are Waves?
- Waves come in different sizes, just like feelings.
- We have both body and brain feelings.

Topic 2: What Are Body Feelings?
- There are eight related senses: touch, vision, hearing, taste, smell, movement, pressure/stretch, and internal body sensations/interoception.
- We can learn to be aware of sensations in our body.

Topic 3: What Are Brain Feelings?
- There are different types of brain feelings and emotions.
- There are different intensities of emotions.

Topic 4: How Are Waves Like Feelings and Emotions?
- There are small waves, medium waves, large waves, and tsunamis of feelings—just like waves in the ocean—coming in different intensities at different times and ultimately passing.
- There are different situations, sensations, activities, tasks, etc. that represent waves for students.

Topic 5: What Do My Waves Look Like?
- Feelings in specific situations lead to different wave sizes.
- We can identify our feelings during daily situations and match them to different waves.

SESSION STARTER

Begin each session with 3–5 minutes of yoga.

belly breathing

flamingo

Yoga Time—Belly Breathing and Flamingo

Introduce yoga and explain that this is a type of exercise that helps your mind be calm. Poses for this unit are belly breathing and flamingo.

- Do the poses at the beginning of each session by showing the pictures and doing the poses with students.
- Hold each pose for a count of five. Have students take slow, deep breaths.
- Encourage students to feel the stretch in different body parts.

COGNITIVE CONCEPTS

Present topics in order, selecting 1–3 activities for each session or lesson.

TOPIC 1: WHAT ARE WAVES?

1. ***Waves, Waves, and More Waves!*** (*Wave Pictures* handout): Use wave pictures and videos (see *Resources*) to compare the sizes of waves and introduce vocabulary: calm waters, small waves, medium waves, large waves, and tsunamis.

2. ***Do The Wave!*** (Sensory Motor—*Do the Wave!* handout): Have you seen people do "The Wave" at a baseball game? Have students practice making different types of waves by doing The Wave at different intensities. Demonstrate each size: **small wave** = wave hands gently down near the ground; **medium wave** = wave arms at waist level in a swaying motion; **large wave** = wave arms forcefully back and forth above head; **tsunami** = wave arms wildly all around. Randomly hold up *Do the Wave!* cards for students.

3. ***Making Waves*** (Sensory Tactile—*Making Waves* handout): Students can use a water bin to experience what causes different-sized waves. Dropping in small or light items (e.g., a pebble, button, paper clip) will barely create a ripple, while dropping in larger or heavier items (e.g., small rock, toy car) will create a larger wave. Students can also explore making different-sized waves with their hands. *Note: Have towels handy for spills or do this outside.*

TOPIC 2: WHAT ARE BODY FEELINGS?

1. ***Feelings in My Body*** (*My Senses* handout; *My Body* pictures): Point to body parts on the *My Body* handout while showing the *My Senses* pictures and discuss the eight senses: touch, taste, hearing, vision, smell, movement, pressure/stretch, internal body sensations/interoception. Students will label the body graphic with word, pictures, or by pasting on the senses pictures.

2. **Sensing My Body** (Sensory Motor—*My Senses* handout; *Sensing My Body* handout): Set up an obstacle course activity by scattering stepping stones (e.g., small plastic floor mats or carpet squares). Each student will jump from one stepping stone to the next, then go to a container and retrieve a *My Senses* picture. Next, the student crawls through a tunnel (or across the floor), spins in a circle two times, and matches the card to a container labeled with a picture of the corresponding body part (e.g., "hungry" goes with "stomach"). You can vary the steps of the obstacle course according to the materials you have available. Activities can include: crawl under, over, or through; go between or around; spin in a chair; bounce on a yoga ball, etc.

TOPIC 3: WHAT ARE BRAIN FEELINGS?

1. **Feelings in My Brain** (*My Brain* handout; *My Emotions* cards): Review the *My Emotions* pictures, explaining that our brains have feelings caused by our thoughts, other people's words or actions, or feelings in our bodies. Sometimes we don't know *why* we feel the way we do. After sharing personal examples of how an event can cause an emotion, help students remember events in their own lives that have caused emotions. Students can draw pictures, write, or cut apart and glue the *My Emotions* pictures on the *My Brain* handout.

2. **Emotion Excavation** (Sensory Tactile—*My Emotions* cards): Have students fold up the *My Emotions* pictures then bury them in a tactile bin full of sand, rice, etc. Students take turns pulling out cards and describing them.

3. **Ocean Emotion Turtle Walk** (Sensory Motor—*My Emotions* cards): Students turtle walk on all fours across the room to retrieve 1-2 *My Emotions* pictures placed 5-10 feet from start point. They then turtle walk back to sit on a bean bag or cushion to name, match, or share information about the card.

TOPIC 4: HOW ARE WAVES LIKE FEELINGS AND EMOTIONS?

1. **Know Your Waves** (*Types of Waves* handout; *Wave Watch* self-rating scale): Prepare by choosing the appropriate *Wave Watch* scale, make copies, and cut apart so that everyone has one. Introduce the *Wave Watch* to students, describing it as a tool we can use to help us identify what our waves look like at any given time. Review the *Types of Waves* handout to deepen understanding, then give examples of situations in which we might want to identify our wave size and have students practice using the wave scale.

2. **Shave the Waves** (Sensory Tactile—*Shave the Waves* handout): Use shaving cream on a tray or tabletop. Have students use popsicle sticks or fingers to draw the different waves from the handout. Have students draw small waves, medium waves, large waves, and tsunamis.

3. **Ocean Motion** (Sensory Motor): Turn on music and have students dance, hop, jump, run, or walk at different rates, heights, and intensities to match the wave types from the *Types of Waves* handout (e.g., jumping in the air or on a mini trampoline for large waves; slow, linear movement, like rocking, for calm waters). Help students connect more intense movements to higher waves and more intense feelings.

TOPIC 5: WHAT DO MY WAVES LOOK LIKE?

1. **Check Out My Waves** (*Wave Monitor* handout): Students will learn that different waves are reactions to varied feelings and experiences. They will match emotional states to wave types by choosing wave sizes. Provide support and guidance while understanding that answers will be different for different students. Explain that waves, like emotions and thoughts, are temporary and will change throughout the day. By understanding their own waves, students can begin to figure out how to manage, or ride, them.

2. **What Is My Wave?** (*Wave Tracker* handout): Students practice associating feelings with waves sizes by reading the specific situations and descriptions of feelings, then placing a check mark in the column for the wave size that best matches that situation and feeling.

3. **Squishy Fishy** (Sensory Tactile): Make beach- or ocean-themed squish bags. Use blue hair gel or clear shampoo and fill a resealable gallon bag. Place a small amount of glitter, beads, gems, or plastic ocean items (e.g., shells, fish, etc.) and seal the bag with duct tape. Students can press and squeeze the bags into different wave sizes while describing their feelings when waves are small (calm, alert, interested, etc.) and when waves are big (excited, upset, angry, etc.).

MINDFULNESS SESSION ENDER

End each session with one of the following mindfulness activities.

MINDFUL BREATHING

Mindful breathing is one of the easiest and best strategies to help us clear our minds and calm our bodies. Use mindful breathing at the end of a session by having students sit comfortably and then read the following script slowly, with short pauses between sentences. Use a calm and steady voice:

(Continued on next page.)

- *Breathe slowly through your nose.*
- *Feel your tummy push out. Think about how the air feels.*
- *Relax as you breathe slowly. Feel your feet relax as you take a breath.*
- *Relax your hands as you breathe.*
- *Feel your tummy push out as you take a slow, deep breath.*
- *Keep thinking about breathing slowly. If another thought comes into your mind, push it away with your next breath. Think only about breathing slowly and relaxing your body.*

MINDFUL TOUCH

Have each student hold an ocean object (a small seashell or plain rock). Ask them to sit in a comfortable position, then read the following script slowly, with short pauses between sentences. Use a calm and steady voice:

- *Breathe slowly through your nose.*
- *Feel your tummy push out.*
- *Think about how the object feels. Is it bumpy or smooth? Is it heavy or light? Does it feel flat or round? Hold it gently. How does it feel in your hand?*
- *Keep thinking about your ocean object. If another thought comes into your mind, push it away and think about your object.*
- *Breathe slowly as you think only about your ocean object.*

RESOURCES

Unit 1 Topic 1.1
Types of Waves

3:00 m

https://www.youtube.com/watch?v=N4aBYmQXPzc

Unit 1 Topic 1.1
How Are Waves Made in the Ocean?

5:00 m

https://www.youtube.com/watch?v=hVoz7mkVhx4

Unit 1 Topic 1.1
How Do Ocean Waves Work?

4:00 m

https://www.youtube.com/watch?v=_LRc6k-clzE&t=121s

Unit 1 Topics 1-5

Handouts

https://drive.google.com/drive/folders/1o2sc7fMLDGtN8DabsTDvZcmhWRejfwOl?usp=drive_link

YOGA TIME

BELLY BREATHING POSE

FLAMINGO POSE

Let's do **belly breathing pose**:
- Sit on the floor with your legs criss-crossed.
- Take a deep breath . . . hold . . . release.
- Hold your arms to the side.
- Sit with your back straight and head up.
- Hold your hands out, palms up.
- Take one last deep breath . . . hold . . . release.

Let's do **flamingo pose**:
- Stand with your feet apart.
- Take a slow, deep breath.
- Put one foot on your calf and hold.
- Reach your arms above your head.
- Bring your hands together.
- You are standing like a flamingo.
- Breathe slowly.
- Take one last deep breath . . . hold . . . release.

WAVE PICTURES

CALM WATER
small ripples in water

SMALL WAVES
small ridges or swells that
come up to your knees

MEDIUM WAVES
deeper waves that
start to get rough

LARGE WAVES
taller waves that
come close together

TSUNAMI
a wall of water as
big as a mountain

DO THE WAVE!

Directions: Demonstrate and have students practice making waves: **small wave** = move hands gently down near the ground; **medium wave** = move arms at waist level in a swaying motion; **large wave** = move arms forcefully back and forth above head; **tsunami** = move arms wildly all around. Then, randomly hold up game cards (below) as students cycle through the different waves.

SMALL WAVE

MEDIUM WAVE

LARGE WAVE

TSUNAMI

MAKING WAVES

MATERIALS

- **Plastic tub or bin**
- **Flat surface** (tabletop or floor)
- **Light and heavy objects**

  Light objects: button, paper clip, plastic chips, pebble, small shell, etc.

  Heavy objects: small or medium rock, toy car, large shell, etc.

DIRECTIONS

1. Fill tub/bin half way with water and place on a flat surface.
2. Demonstrate: Drop light objects in the water and comment on the small ripples. Describe what you see and encourage students to describe the small ripples in the water.
3. Demonstrate: Drop heavy objects in the water and comment on the splash and waves you see. Describe what you notice and encourage students to describe the larger waves in the water.
4. Have students make different-sized waves with their hands in the water bin.

SUGGESTED QUESTIONS TO ASK STUDENTS

1. What happens when we drop light objects into the water?
2. What happens when we drop heavy objects into the water?
3. How do we make small waves in the water?
4. How do we make large waves in the water?

POSSIBLE OBJECTS

MY SENSES

Directions: Point to each sense and identify the location on your own body.

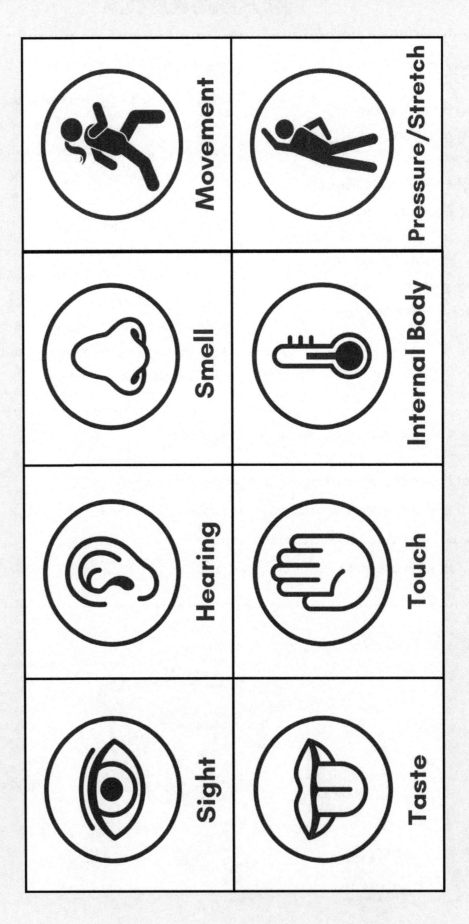

MY BODY

Directions: Label eight senses on the graphic below by writing the word, drawing pictures, or using the *My Senses* pictures at the bottom of the page. Hint—add whole body senses on the left.

Sight

Hearing

Smell

Movement

Taste

Touch

Internal Body

Pressure/Stretch

63

SENSING MY BODY

MATERIALS

- **Floor markers:** Plastic non-slip mats
- *My Senses* **pictures, bin:** Set of *My Senses* pictures cut into cards and placed in a bin
- **Bowls or tubs:** Label with *Body Parts* (below) for matching
- **Obstacle course:** Use items such as a tunnel, carpet squares, tape, yoga ball, spinning chair, etc.

DIRECTIONS

1. Make the obstacle course: lay out plastic mats so students may step or hop from one to the next; put a bin of *My Senses* pictures at the last mat; place bowls labeled with one *Body Parts* card each (see cards below) at the end of the obstacle course for matching.

2. Students complete the first part of the obstacle course to retrieve a *My Senses* pictures card. Holding the card, they complete an action (crawl through a tunnel, bounce on a yoga ball, spin on a chair, go under a table, etc.) and match the card to the body part by placing it in the correct bowl. (Note: Internal Body, Movement, and Pressure/Stretch match to "Body.")

BODY PARTS

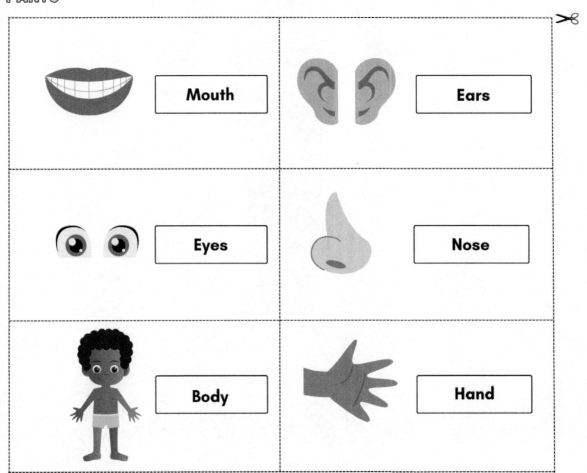

© Tracey DeMaria, Autism Moving Forward

MY BRAIN

Directions: Remember 2-3 events in your life that have caused emotions, then identify these emotions with the *My Emotions* pictures by placing them (cut & glue) on this handout. Note: Smaller *My Emotions* cards are available in the Appendix. Optional activity: Draw pictures and/or write about your emotions.

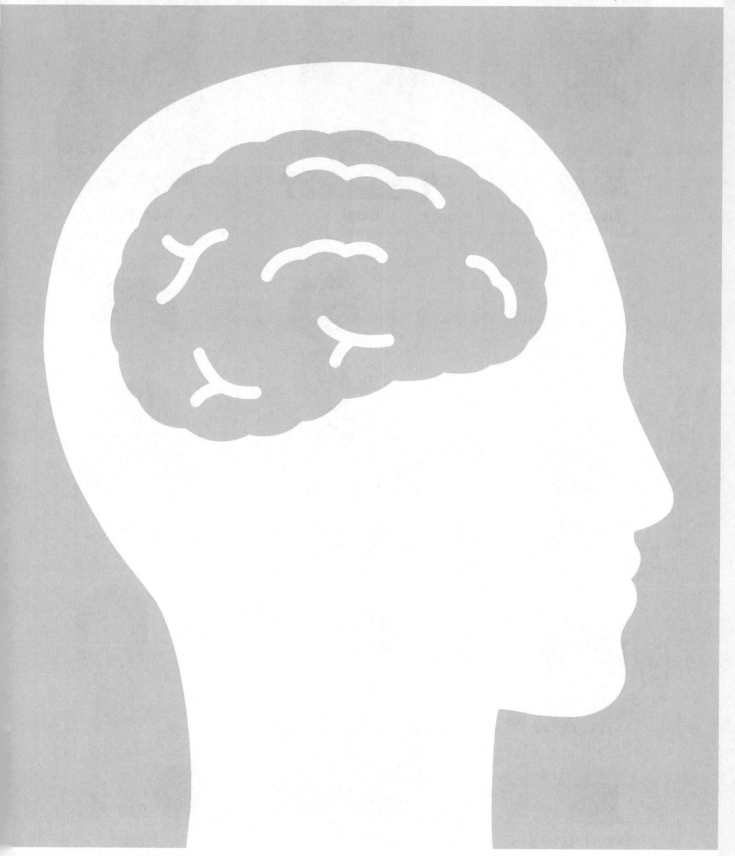

65

MY EMOTIONS

happy

sad

scared

mad

surprised

calm

frustrated

anxious

tired

MY EMOTIONS (SMALLER)

 scared

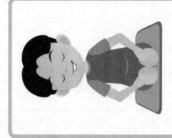 calm

 tired

 sad

 surprised

 anxious

 happy

 mad

 frustrated

 scared

 calm

 tired

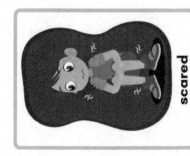 sad

 surprised

 anxious

 happy

 mad

 frustrated

 happy

TYPES OF WAVES

Instructor directions: Read the introduction and descriptions of each wave size with the students. Give personal examples and ask students to share a time they have experienced each wave size.

Introduction: *Our feelings are like waves on the ocean, sometimes incredibly big and overwhelming and sometimes small and manageable. All waves can represent positive or negative feelings. Different situations can create different waves.*

Calm Water

Calm waters are relaxed feelings of energy in your body and brain. These are the times when you are in a calm and alert state, ready to work or play in a regulated mindset. Situations and events happen around you. You are coping and adapting and ready to go about your day.

Small Waves

Small waves are slight feelings of energy, distress, and discomfort that can lead to little highs and lows. They are manageable with the right responses.
Possible triggers:
- Lunchtime, bus rides, low mood or energy
- Transition times between activities
- Unstructured activities—recess, games, sports
- Non-preferred activities and classwork

Medium Waves

Medium waves are moderate feelings of energy, distress, and discomfort that make your brain and body feel uncomfortable. Medium waves can turn into large waves.
Possible triggers:
- Transitions or unexpected changes
- Changing from preferred to non-preferred activities or classwork
- Loud or bright environment

Large Waves

Large waves are big feelings of high energy, distress, and discomfort that can turn into meltdowns or extreme reactions and behaviors. Large waves can turn into tsunamis. Possible triggers:
- Being told "no"; ending screen time; change in plans
- Difficult tasks and homework; perceived loss
- Arguments or conflict with others; social situations that cause stress
- Loud environments; feeling sick; very tired

Tsunami

Tsunamis are giant and dangerous waves. Tsunamis happen when you feel out of control and in crisis. During a tsunami, you may need assistance to stay safe and feel better. Often, a tsunami immediately follows a large wave that is not navigated effectively.

WAVE WATCH

Instructor directions: Below are three examples of the *Wave Watch* visual tool. Choose the version that best supports the individual needs and skills of each student. Have students use the *Wave Watch* to help them understand and then begin to rate the intensity of their feelings. Students can keep their *Wave Watch* on their desks or carry it throughout the day. (Note: Printable pages with multiple copies of the same version are available in the *Appendix*.)

WAVE WATCH

Calm Water	Small Waves	Medium Waves	Large Waves	Tsunami
			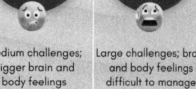	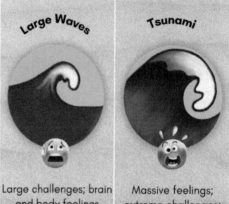
Feeling okay—no brain or body challenges	Small challenges; brain and body feelings	Medium challenges; bigger brain and body feelings	Large challenges; brain and body feelings difficult to manage	Massive feelings; extreme challenges; too much—I need help

WAVE WATCH

Calm Water	Small Waves	Medium Waves	Large Waves	Tsunami

Feeling okay—no brain or body challenges	Small challenges; brain and body feelings	Medium challenges; bigger brain and body feelings	Large challenges; brain and body feelings difficult to manage	Massive feelings; extreme challenges; too much—I need help

WAVE WATCH

Calm Water	Small Waves	Medium Waves	Large Waves	Tsunami
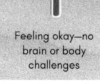				
1	2	3	4	5
Feeling okay—no brain or body challenges	Small challenges; brain and body feelings	Medium challenges; bigger brain and body feelings	Large challenges; brain and body feelings difficult to manage	Massive feelings; extreme challenges; too much—I need help

WAVE WATCH
WAVES WITH EMOJIS

WAVE WATCH

Calm Water	Small Waves	Medium Waves	Large Waves	Tsunami
		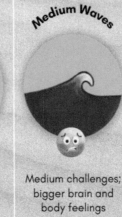		
Feeling okay—no brain or body challenges	Small challenges; brain and body feelings	Medium challenges; bigger brain and body feelings	Large challenges; brain and body feelings difficult to manage	Massive feelings; extreme challenges; too much—I need help

WAVE WATCH

Calm Water	Small Waves	Medium Waves	Large Waves	Tsunami
	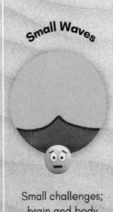			
Feeling okay—no brain or body challenges	Small challenges; brain and body feelings	Medium challenges; bigger brain and body feelings	Large challenges; brain and body feelings difficult to manage	Massive feelings; extreme challenges; too much—I need help

WAVE WATCH

Calm Water	Small Waves	Medium Waves	Large Waves	Tsunami
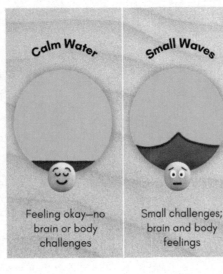				
Feeling okay—no brain or body challenges	Small challenges; brain and body feelings	Medium challenges; bigger brain and body feelings	Large challenges; brain and body feelings difficult to manage	Massive feelings; extreme challenges; too much—I need help

WAVE WATCH
WAVES ONLY

WAVE WATCH

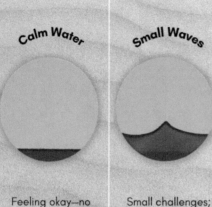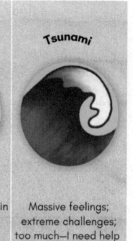

Calm Water	Small Waves	Medium Waves	Large Waves	Tsunami
Feeling okay—no brain or body challenges	Small challenges; brain and body feelings	Medium challenges; bigger brain and body feelings	Large challenges; brain and body feelings difficult to manage	Massive feelings; extreme challenges; too much—I need help

WAVE WATCH

Calm Water	Small Waves	Medium Waves	Large Waves	Tsunami
Feeling okay—no brain or body challenges	Small challenges; brain and body feelings	Medium challenges; bigger brain and body feelings	Large challenges; brain and body feelings difficult to manage	Massive feelings; extreme challenges; too much—I need help

WAVE WATCH

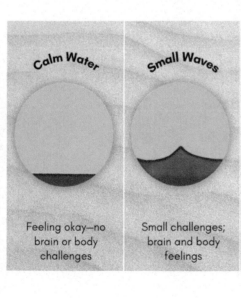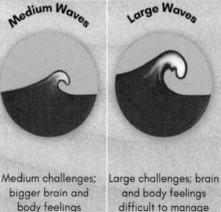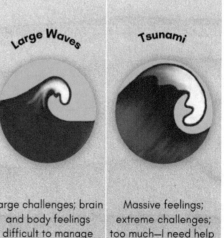

Calm Water	Small Waves	Medium Waves	Large Waves	Tsunami
Feeling okay—no brain or body challenges	Small challenges; brain and body feelings	Medium challenges; bigger brain and body feelings	Large challenges; brain and body feelings difficult to manage	Massive feelings; extreme challenges; too much—I need help

WAVE WATCH
WAVES WITH NUMBERS

WAVE WATCH

  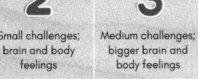  

Calm Water — **1** — Feeling okay—no brain or body challenges

Small Waves — **2** — Small challenges; brain and body feelings

Medium Waves — **3** — Medium challenges; bigger brain and body feelings

Large Waves — **4** — Large challenges; brain and body feelings difficult to manage

Tsunami — **5** — Massive feelings; extreme challenges; too much—I need help

WAVE WATCH

 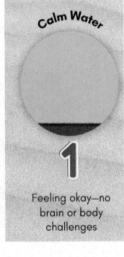    

Calm Water — **1** — Feeling okay—no brain or body challenges

Small Waves — **2** — Small challenges; brain and body feelings

Medium Waves — **3** — Medium challenges; bigger brain and body feelings

Large Waves — **4** — Large challenges; brain and body feelings difficult to manage

Tsunami — **5** — Massive feelings; extreme challenges; too much—I need help

WAVE WATCH

    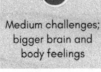  

Calm Water — **1** — Feeling okay—no brain or body challenges

Small Waves — **2** — Small challenges; brain and body feelings

Medium Waves — **3** — Medium challenges; bigger brain and body feelings

Large Waves — **4** — Large challenges; brain and body feelings difficult to manage

Tsunami — **5** — Massive feelings; extreme challenges; too much—I need help

SHAVE THE WAVE

Directions: Use fingers or popsicle sticks to trace waves with shaving cream. Can you describe the size of each wave?

WAVE MONITOR

Directions: Read the situations and decide how you would feel or react. Then describe your emotions and choose a wave on the *Wave Watch*.

1. riding the bus to school
2. doing homework
3. eating in the cafeteria
4. going to recess
5. participating in group activities
6. free time with favorite activity

WAVE WATCH

Calm Water
Feeling okay—no brain or body challenges

Small Waves
Small challenges; brain and body feelings

Medium Waves
Medium challenges; bigger brain and body feelings

Large Waves
Large challenges; brain and body feelings difficult to manage

Tsunami
Massive feelings; extreme challenges; too much—I need help

WAVE TRACKER

Directions: Next to each emotional state, point to or mark the column for the wave that best fits.

Situations	Calm Water	Small Waves	Medium Waves	Large Waves	Tsunami
1. I feel good. I just finished my work and I can pick an activity.					
2. My friend said we can't hang out today. I'm sad.					
3. It's my birthday and I'm really excited and happy. I'm feeling hyper and I keep laughing.					
4. The fire alarm went off and I am scared. I am feeling stressed and very overwhelmed. I want to run out of class.					
5. I am so tired. It was noisy last night and I was awake all night.					
6. My friend is moving next week. I am so sad. I also feel worried because I am not sure who I can hang out with at school.					
7. During math I was annoyed because everyone kept talking. It was too noisy to do my work and now I am stressed.					
8. (Make up your own.)					

UNIT 2: SURFING AND SURFBOARDS

INTRODUCTION

Unit 2 teaches what it means to surf the waves of feelings in our brain and body, and how surfboard tools represent the strategies we need to surf these waves.

- Topic 1 is about how surfing the waves means riding them until they pass.
- Topic 2 describes positive and negative feelings and how they are like waves.
- Topic 3 explains surfboard tools for the body and sensory system.
- Topic 4 explains surfboard tools for the brain.
- Topic 5 helps us select the best tools to successfully navigate waves throughout the day.

OBJECTIVES

Students will master the following concepts:

Topic 1: How Can I Surf the Waves?
- Just as surfers ride on top of waves, we can use surfboard tools to surf our own waves of emotions throughout the day, riding waves until they pass.
- Surfboard tools are body and brain strategies that can help us surf our waves.

Topic 2: How Can I Surf Waves of Feelings?
- Everyone has positive and negative feelings, and everyone experiences them differently.
- Feelings sometimes don't match a situation, and that can make surfing harder.

Topic 3: What Are Surfboard Tools for the Body?
- Surfboard tools for the body involve all eight sensory systems.
- Body tools also support general health and wellness.

Topic 4: What Are Surfboard Tools for the Brain?
- Surfboard tools for the brain help us think about what we are doing.
- Brain tools affect our thoughts and emotions and help us feel more regulated.

Topic 5: What Surfboard Tools Work Best for You?
- We all have our own surfboard, but we need the right tools to help us surf our waves.
- We all surf differently based on our regulation needs.

SESSION STARTER

Begin each session with 3-5 minutes of yoga.

Yoga Time—Down Dog and Up Dog

Introduce the yoga poses and remind students that yoga is a type of exercise that helps your mind be calm. Poses for this unit are down dog and up dog.

- Do the poses at the beginning of each session by showing the pictures and doing the poses with students.
- Hold each pose for a count of five. Have each student take slow, deep breaths.
- Encourage students to feel the stretch in different body parts.

WAVE WATCH CHECK-IN

- Use the *Wave Watch* to have students indicate their current feelings by selecting a wave (calm water, small wave, medium wave, large wave, tsunami) or corresponding number before beginning the cognitive activities.
- Explore why students chose a certain wave, especially if they always choose the same wave. You can share examples of how your own waves change from day to day.
- You can use the *Wave Watch* at the start and end of the lesson to help students identify changes in their waves after activities.

COGNITIVE CONCEPTS

Present topics in order, selecting 1-3 activities for each session or lesson.

TOPIC 1: HOW CAN I SURF THE WAVES?

1. ***Brave the Waves*** (*Surfing Pictures* handout): Look at the pictures and watch some of the videos found in *Resources*. Have students reflect on what they see. Then discuss the following questions:
   - *What do you notice about the waves? How are they different?* (Possible answers: some are bigger/smaller, stronger/weaker, more whitecaps, faster/slower) *How are feelings like this?*
   - *Would you surf all of these waves the same way? How would you do it differently if the wave was strong and fast instead of a small, slow wave? Do we surf or deal with our feelings in the same way every time?*

- *Are there good or bad waves? How about feelings?*

2. **Hang Ten, Dude!** (Sensory Motor): Students pretend to surf by completing these steps:
   - **Step 1:** Imitate "hanging ten" by standing and balancing with arms out. Progress to a surfing stance on a cushion or balance board.
   - **Step 2:** Use a swing, scooter, trampoline, yoga ball, or other type of equipment to demonstrate different ways to surf (crouch low, stand up, etc.).
   - **Step 3:** Ask students to think about how balancing and moving on the equipment are like balancing and moving on water like a surfer.

3. **Shaping My Surfboard** (*My Surfboard* handout): Surfboards can be different sizes and shapes in order to better surf certain kinds of waves. (For example, shortboards are good for turns and movement, while longboards are more stable and easier to paddle.) Show pictures of different surfboards (e.g., colors, shapes, and styles) then have students decorate their own *My Surfboard* graphic, using markers, stickers, washi tape, or any art material. Students can compare their surfboards, noticing how they are all different but can all ride waves.

TOPIC 2: HOW DO YOU SURF WAVES OF FEELINGS?

1. **How Would You Feel?** (*Feelings Match-Up* handout): Introduce the activity sheet, explaining that we sometimes react to situations in different ways. Students should select the situation that would most likely cause that emotion for them. Students may have different answers for what they think is the best match, because everyone has different feelings. It's okay if some individuals make unexpected choices.

2. **Emotions in Motion** (*Feeling Faces* handout): Students go over the chart on the handout and then act out the feelings and emotions. Have students watch others demonstrate the various emotions, including in person or on video. Point out specific facial expressions and body movements for each emotion.

3. **Mirror, Mirror** (*My Own Emotions* handout): Students look at their faces in a mirror while they act out different emotions. They then can draw themselves on the *My Own Emotions* activity sheet. Discuss recent events at home or in the classroom, reflecting on the feelings that happened, e.g., "I saw you running with your friends outside. Your voice was loud and you were smiling. What were you feeling?" People feel and show emotions in different ways, e.g., some people may yell when they are mad, but others may cry or simply walk away.

TOPIC 3: WHAT ARE SURFBOARD TOOLS FOR THE BODY?

1. **My Body Can Surf the Waves** (*Surfboard Tools for the Body* handout): Review the handout and ask students to decide which surfboard tools might work best for them. Surfboard tools for the body include input to any of the eight sensory systems, as well as general health and wellness tools. Tools for the body can include getting enough sleep, jumping, running, having a snack, stretching, or drinking water.

2. **Exploring My Senses** (*Eight Ways to Explore Your Senses* handout): Have students actively explore all eight sensory systems by presenting them with the items and activities suggested in each section of the *Eight Ways to Explore Your Senses* handout. The goal is to have students experience their senses while beginning to understand what they do and don't like. This activity will require more than one lesson or session. Note: The handout is optional for students.

TOPIC 4: WHAT ARE SURFBOARD TOOLS FOR THE BRAIN?

1. **I've Got Surfing on the Brain** (*Surfboard Tools for the Brain* handout): Review the handout and ask students to decide which surfboard tools for the brain might work best for them. Encourage students to share special interests or topics they enjoy talking about, as these are often good brain tools (e.g., specific characters, dinosaurs, planets, computers, animé, games).

2. **I'm a Sea Star** (*Affirmations* handout; *Affirmations Cards* handout): Have students read the *Affirmation Cards* activity sheet, then cut and paste the cards onto the ocean scene. The affirmation cards can be printed and laminated for students to keep in their desk or backpack. They can also come up with their own affirmations on the blank surfboards. After they have finished, have students take turns sharing one of their affirmations.

3. **Wave Breathing** (*Breathe With the Wave* handout): Have students use this exercise as a calming tool. Guide them through the directions on the wave graphic, having them use their fingers or a small item (e.g., mini surfboard) to trace up and down the wave. Show students how to breathe in as the wave goes up and breathe out as the wave crest goes down.

TOPIC 5: WHAT ARE SURFBOARD TOOLS FOR THE BODY?

1. **My Surfboard Toolkit** (*Surfboard Preference List* handout): Read the list of strategies on the handout and have students discuss how helpful or important each tool is for surfing their own waves. It is helpful for students to understand which tools work for them and which do not. Students can also add their own tools to each section.

2. ***What Are My Strengths and Challenges?*** (*Strengths and Challenges* handout): Have students generate their own list of personal strengths and skills on the activity sheet. Knowing our strengths and challenges helps us plan how to surf the waves. Next, have each student list at least one personal challenge or something that is hard for them. Be sensitive when discussing body or brain feelings that you think may be challenges for the students.

3. ***How Am I Doing?*** (*Surfer Rating Scale* handout; *Surfer Rating Scale—Sample* handout): Review the sample *Surfer Rating Scale*, explaining the Wave Levels and each Daily Activity on the chart. Talk about the sample student ratings and describe the wave level that may represent the emotion for each daily activity.

   For example, "Participating in a group activity was very scary and stressful and caused a large wave." "I ate my favorite food in a quiet area of the lunch room. I felt comfortable so it felt like calm water."

   Have students rate their own daily activities over several weeks on the *Surfer Rating Scale*, or as needed, with monitoring and support.

   ○ **Note:** It is critical that students NOT be given the message that rating themselves as feeling or experiencing a tsunami (5) is "bad" and that calm water (1) is "good." This process is about teaching students that we all have big and small waves in our day. The better we get at understanding them, the easier it will become to surf them.

MINDFULNESS SESSION ENDER

End each session with one mindfulness activity.

MINDFUL OCEAN OBSERVATIONS

Have each student lie flat on their back with their head on a pillow or rolled towel to give a clear view of their belly. The student then places the surfboard* (e.g., toy, popsicle stick, or paper cutout) on the center of their belly and rests their arms flat next to their body.
Use a clear and steady voice:

- *Breathe in slowly through your nose.*
- *Watch your belly push out.*
- *Let the air out and see your belly go down again.*
- *Breathe in and out—your belly moves up and down like waves in the ocean.*
- *Look at your surfboard moving on your belly as you breathe.*
- *Notice the shape, the color, and the size of your surfboard.*
- *Breathe in and out and watch your surfboard ride the waves.*
- *You can take this calm feeling with you as you surf your waves throughout the day.*

*Before starting, provide students with a small surfboard (e.g., small plastic surfboard toy, popsicle stick, paper surfboard, etc.).

Student support: The surfboard for this exercise will help students focus on their breathing by looking, touching, or exploring it with their hands. Provide the surfboard to the student or their lifeguard (helping adult) for practice and use.

MINDFUL BREATHING—PINWHEEL

This is an exercise for younger children or students who would benefit from more practice breathing in and out.

- Give students the a copy of the pinwheel handout.
- Students can color the pinwheel with scented markers, or markers of choice.
- If scents are used, have students smell the scents on the paper to practice breathing in.
- Next, have students blow on the pinwheel to pretend they are making it spin.
- Have students practice taking deep breaths in to smell and blowing out to spin the pinwheel.

Alternative to scented markers: Students can color with regular markers then use a cotton swab to add a scented lotion or lip balm to the pinwheel (to be used only for scent, not lips).

Tip: If available, use a real pinwheel to show the students how they work.

RESOURCES

Unit 1 Topic 1.1
Beginner Surf
Lessons

Video of preschooler paddling—4:02 m

https://youtu.be/AolC
uwJT2SI

Unit 1 Topic 1.1
Huge Surf Airs

Video of 10-year-old surfing—1:31 m

https://youtu.be/c0Z
2TY609ac

Unit 1 Topic 1.1
Teenage Surfing
Lesson

Video of teenagers surfing— 1:00 m

https://youtu.be/oWM
Ws0fPTWQ

Unit 2 Topics 1-5

Handouts

https://drive.google.com
/drive/folders/1PRQkO7Is
0bAfvyLobWqEfnSOtCuDI
_dO?usp=drive_link

YOGA TIME

UP DOG POSE

Let's do **up dog pose**:

- Lie flat on the floor on your tummy with arms at your sides.
- Bring your arms up beside your head.
- Take slow, deep breaths.
- Bend your elbows and lift your chest as you pull back your arms.
- Lift up your head and look forward.
- Stretch your legs and point your toes.
- Take one last deep breath . . . hold . . . release.

DOWN DOG POSE

Let's do **down dog pose**:

- Lie flat on the floor on your tummy—head up.
- Come up on your hands and knees.
- Take slow, deep breaths.
- Curl your toes into the floor and push your hips into the air.
- Stretch your legs straight and hang your head between strong arms.
- Take one last deep breath . . . hold . . . release.

SURFING PICTURES

MY SURFBOARD

Directions: Decorate your own surfboard using markers, stickers, washi tape, or any art material. Then compare your surfboard with other students', noticing how they might be different but can all ride waves.

85

FEELINGS MATCH-UP

Directions: Choose the situation that is the best match for the feeling. Note—it is okay to have different answers since everyone should match the feeling and situation that works best for them.

Feeling	Situation	Situation
1. I feel tired and sleepy.	a. Getting ready for bed	b. Working with my math group
2. I am full of energy.	a. Doing my homework	b. Playing with friends
3. I am mad and upset.	a. Lining up for lunch	b. Classmate called me a name
4. I am jealous and frustrated.	a. Our team lost the game	b. Lunchroom ran out of pizza
5. I feel scared.	a. Waiting to be picked up	b. Taking a math test
6. I am worried.	a. Going back to class after recess	b. I have no one to play with
7. I am sad.	a. My best friend is absent today	b. The classroom is loud and noisy
8. I am calm and happy.	a. I finished all my homework	b. Our team is winning the game

FEELING FACES

Directions: Review the emotions in each picture then act out each one.

Angry	Happy	Confused	Sad

Tired	Nervous	Scared	Surprised

MY OWN EMOTIONS

Directions: Look at your face in the mirror while acting out each emotion. Draw how your emotions look on the faces below.

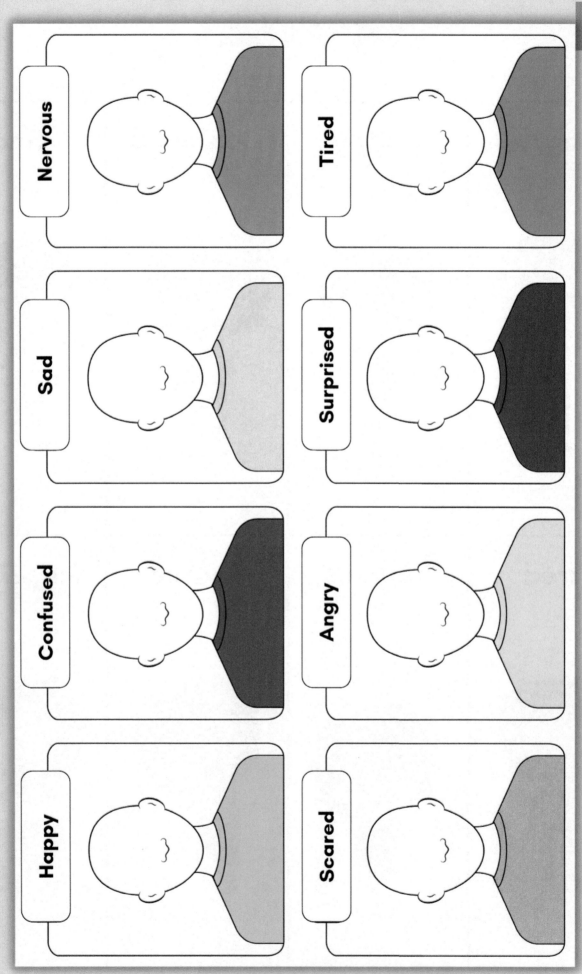

Happy

Confused

Sad

Nervous

Scared

Angry

Surprised

Tired

SURFBOARD TOOLS
for the BODY

Instructor: Use this to guide discussion or you can hand out the page to students.

Body Tools

- **Do heavy muscle work:** Jump, crash, climb, push, pull, stretch, do yoga, use weighted items, deep pressure massage, head/hand/arm/leg/foot squeezes, or compression clothing. This is the most powerful tool for surfing all waves!

- **Get your body moving:** Walk, run, swing, skip, dance, spin, rock on your foot or in chair, bounce or roll on yoga ball, ride bike/scooter, stand on balance board, do obstacle courses.

- **Mouth:** Crunchy and/or chewy foods, chew tubes or necklaces, other safe non-food items to chew on, sour or spicy tastes for intensity.

- **Ears:** Noise-canceling headphones to decrease background noise, calming music (60 beats/minute), white noise to help with background noise, Tibetan bowl or chime, preferred music to help with mood and distraction.

- **Eyes:** Avoid bright, florescent, and flashing lights; calm by using dim, muted, and steady lights. Light or spinning toys (color-changing, flashlights), sand toys, toys with falling or spilling (sand from hand into bin, water through funnel). Clutter-free work area, few visual distractions, wear sunglasses inside and outside.

- **Touch and feel:** Play dough, slime, goo, sand, putty, moon sand, kinetic sand, shaving cream, lotion. Pops-its, stress balls, squishy items, water tubes, stuffed animals or soft plush toys, fabric. Dry vs. wet (i.e., chalk/sand/flour on hands vs. sticky, slimy, or mushy items). Hot vs. cold (i.e., ice packs, warm packs).

- **Smell:** Calming scents (lavender, vanilla) vs. more alerting scents (mint, orange), but individual preferences matter most! Use natural items if possible—chemicals can be too strong and unhealthy. Limit or avoid fragrances or perfumes.

- **Internal sensations:** Are you hungry or thirsty? Do you feel tired or awake? Breathing slow or fast? Need to use the bathroom? Need to use it more frequently? Does your head feel buzzy or foggy? In pain or sick? Get enough sleep, drink fluids, and eat healthy foods.

EIGHT WAYS TO EXPLORE YOUR SENSES

Instructor: Have students try these activities, then ask them the questions at the end of each section.

Tactile—Touch	Explore items that are: • Wet, dry, soft, hard, smooth, slimy, bumpy, etc. For example: shaving cream, sand, rice, beans, sandpaper, soft fabrics, smooth rocks, bumpy textured balls. • Use a warm wet cloth, then ice or cold water to explore hot vs. cold. *Which textures do you like or dislike? Think of times when things are hot or cold.*
Auditory—Sound	Present or simulate different sounds with music or audio recordings: • Listen to different volumes, speed, and high/low tones (deep drum vs. high cymbal). • Listen to voices, shouting vs. whispering. • Listen to different environmental noises (fire alarms, air conditioner). *Do these sounds make you feel calm, alert, or agitated?*
Pressure and Stretch 	Try doing different types of heavy work with your body: • Push hands together against each other with arms up and elbows out or do wall push-ups. • Holding bent arms in front of you, clasp hands by fingertips and pull in opposite directions. • Use your body against gravity—Superman pose: lay on your belly with arms and legs extended out and up. Next, try weight-bearing postures, such as wheelbarrow walks and animal walks. • Explore deep pressure by gently squeezing the muscle area of your own forearms or biceps. Try squeezing or pressure with bean bags or pillows (if tolerated). *Do your muscles feel different? Are they tense, relaxed, or something else?*
Vestibular—Movement	Try different types of movement: • Run in place, alternating between slow and fast. • Spin in a circle three times while standing. • Sit on the floor or on a chair and gently rock forward-backward, then side-to-side. *Did these movements make your head feel dizzy, calm, excited, or something else?*
Oral Sensory—Taste or Mouth	Explore food* and non-food oral items, and note student responses: • Present food with various textures and tastes—chewy, crunchy, smooth, salty, sweet, spicy, sour. • Explore non-food oral items such as whistles, straws, oral sensory tools, and blowing bubbles. *If not able to use actual food items, you can discuss food preferences and experiences.* *Follow all food allergy precautions. Respect aversions and never force a child to eat anything.
Olfactory—Smell	Explore various smells and aromas:* • Use natural scents when possible. • Try coffee beans, citrus (lemon, orange), fresh herbs (lavender, sage, rosemary), cinnamon, vanilla, bubblegum, spices, etc. *Discuss different reactions and preferences to scents.* *Be aware of sensitivities, as some scents trigger agitation and headaches.
Interoception—Internal Body Sensations	Talk with students about how their different organs feel inside their bodies: • Put your hand on your chest. Feel your heartbeat and your breathing. • Talk about how it feels when you need to use the bathroom (pressure in bladder or bowels). • How does the temperature feel in your body? How do you feel when it is very hot or really cold? *What parts of your body do you feel when you are hungry or sick?*

SURFBOARD TOOLS
for the BRAIN

Instructor: Use this to guide discussion or you can hand out the page to students.

- **Have a conversation:** Talk to a friend or someone else about how you are feeling or what is on your mind.

- **Storytelling:** Write or tell a story, write in a journal, tell someone about your favorite game or subject, draw a picture, make a video. If you are uncomfortable, use writing or typing tools.

- **Screen time:** Too much unstructured screen time can be overstimulating or even addictive, but you can carefully use screen time to redirect your brain with video games, tablets, computer. Be careful not to watch something that you know can upset you or be overstimulating. Avoid screen time for an hour before bedtime.

- **Read or listen to a book you enjoy:** Books, magazines, comic books.

- **Puzzles or other brain games:** Sudoku, word searches, cryptograms, mazes, crosswords, jigsaw puzzles.

- **Mindfulness tools:** Do mindful breathing, watch a mindfulness video, do a mindfulness activity.

- **Animals or pets:** Cuddle, exercise, or feed your own or a friend's pet.

- **Get organized:** Make a list of goals, activities, or steps, being sure to cross them off when done.

- **Memory work:** Think about your favorite memories—places, special events, times with friends: Who was there? What did it look like? Do you remember noises or smells? Did you eat something yummy?

- **Problem solving:** Review a problem you are having, checking your memories for fact vs. fiction. Do on your own or ask adult for help.

- **Be creative:** Do art projects or crafts, sing a song, try to remember steps to a dance. Coloring books, mandalas, doodling with markers.

- **Learn something new:** Read about a new interest or idea. Memorize a poem or song.

Brain Tools

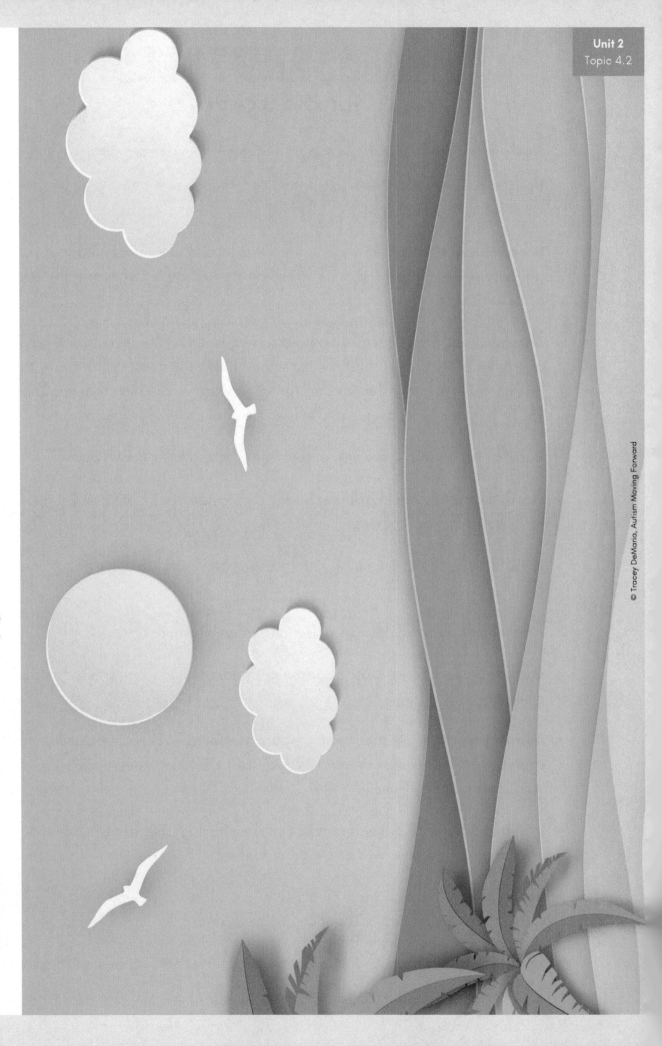

AFFIRMATIONS

Directions: Review the *Affirmation Cards* on the next page, then cut and paste the surfboards onto the beach scene.

AFFIRMATION CARDS

Directions: Cut out the surfboards and paste them on the beach scene from the previous page. These cards can also be printed, laminated, and cut out to keep in your desk or backpack.

I love myself

I am strong

This wave will pass

I can surf this wave

I accept myself

I can do this

I matter

Write your own affirmation on the blank surfboards.

BREATHE WITH THE WAVE

1 Put your finger on the smiley face.

2 As you inhale, trace the curvy wave to the circle that says "HOLD."

3 Hold your breath for a count of three seconds.

4 Slowly exhale and move your finger along the straight line then stop at the smiley face.

Repeat the exercise 3–4 times. Listen to your breathing and compare how it sounds, to the sound of waves.

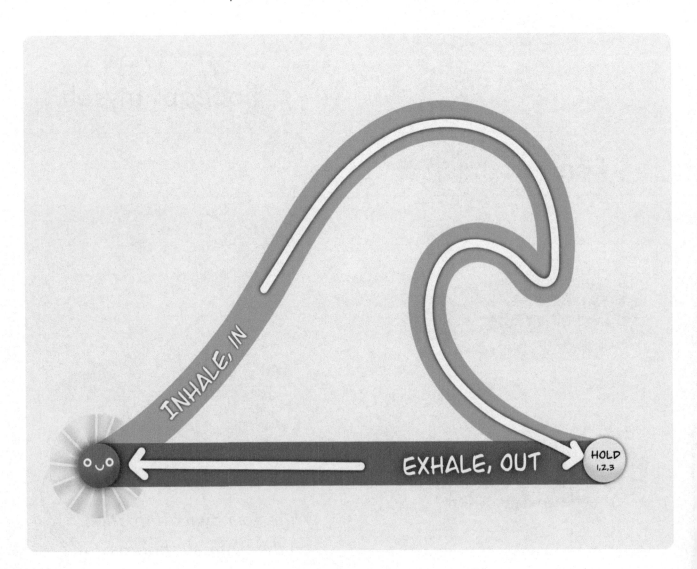

INHALE, IN

EXHALE, OUT

HOLD 1,2,3

Breathe With the Wave

1. Put your finger on the smiley face.
2. As you inhale, trace the curvy wave to the circle that says "HOLD."
3. Hold your breath for a count of three seconds.
4. Slowly exhale and move your finger along the straight line then stop at the smiley face.

Breathe With the Wave

1. Put your finger on the smiley face.
2. As you inhale, trace the curvy wave to the circle that says "HOLD."
3. Hold your breath for a count of three seconds.
4. Slowly exhale and move your finger along the straight line then stop at the smiley face.

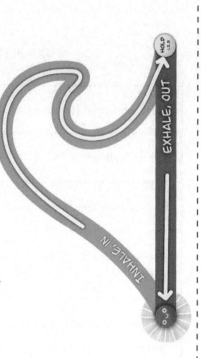

Breathe With the Wave

1. Put your finger on the smiley face.
2. As you inhale, trace the curvy wave to the circle that says "HOLD."
3. Hold your breath for a count of three seconds.
4. Slowly exhale and move your finger along the straight line then stop at the smiley face.

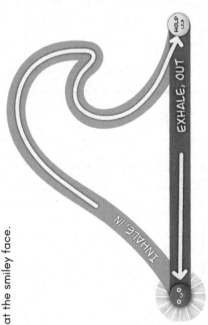

Breathe With the Wave

1. Put your finger on the smiley face.
2. As you inhale, trace the curvy wave to the circle that says "HOLD."
3. Hold your breath for a count of three seconds.
4. Slowly exhale and move your finger along the straight line then stop at the smiley face.

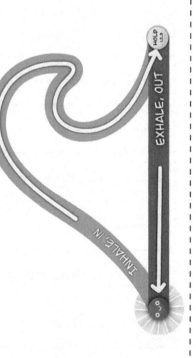

SURFBOARD PREFERENCE LIST

Directions: Read the following list of strategies and think about how helpful or important this tool is when surfing the waves of your day. Add 2-3 of your own tools to each section, and then place + or a – next to the item to show whether it is helpful for you or not. If you haven't tried something, put a **?**.

✚ = HELPFUL ▭ = NOT HELPFUL ？ = HAVEN'T TRIED

Getting eight hours of sleep		Avoiding junk food	
Art activities		Wearing comfortable clothes	
Eating healthy food		Being alone	
Using headphones to block noise		Food: Chewy, crunchy, sour, etc. (circle preference)	
Having a schedule to follow		Playground equipment	
Heavy muscle work (carrying a stack of books, pulling a wagon)		Dim lights vs. bright lights (circle preference)	
Compression or weighted items (blankets, clothing)		Listening to slow music vs. fast music (circle preference)	
Smells (lotions, essential oils)		Mindfulness/meditation	
Exercise, sports		Yoga	
Fidget tools, stress ball		Playing video games	
Reading		Other:	
Relaxation, deep breathing		Other:	
Talking to a friend		Other:	

STRENGTHS AND CHALLENGES

Directions: Look through the list on the next page—what are you good at doing and what is a challenge for you? Add items from the list in the space below. You can write, cut and paste, or dictate your answers.

Strengths: What I'm good at	**Challenges:** What's hard for me

STRENGTHS AND CHALLENGES
continued

Reading	Getting my work done on time
Spelling	Organization
Math	Not being first in line
Writing	Not winning
Waiting	Sense of humor or being funny
Taking turns	Empathy or caring for others
Listening to directions	Memory
Sharing	Puzzles
Running	Good with animals
Sports/athletics	Being artistic
Saying how I feel	Music
Making friends	Handling frustration

SURFER RATING SCALE—SAMPLE

Directions: Review the sample rating scale below, including the *Wave Levels* (left side) and each *Daily Activity* (bottom). Describe possible reasons the sample student marked the wave levels for each activity.

Daily Situations Surfer Rating Scale—Sample

Directions: Mark the box that shows your wave level for your feelings and emotions throughout your day.

Wave Levels	Going to school (bus or car)	Working in a group	Going to recess or break	Eating in lunch room	Doing hard class-work	Giving a wrong answer	Doing home-work	Having free time at home	Other: Read a book
5 Tsunami							X		
4 Large Wave			X					X	
3 Medium Wave				X		X			
2 Small Wave	X								
1 Calm Water		X			X				X

Wave Levels →

Daily Activity →

SURFER RATING SCALE

Directions: Review the rating scale below, including the *Wave Levels* (left side) and each *Daily Activity* (bottom). Rate your wave levels through the day—your teacher or therapist may provide support by asking why you chose the rating level and what feeling or emotion you experienced at that level.

Daily Situations Surfer Rating Scale

Directions: Mark the box that shows your wave level for your feelings and emotions throughout your day.

Wave Levels	Going to school (bus or car)	Working in a group	Going to recess or break	Eating in lunch room	Doing hard class-work	Giving a wrong answer	Doing home-work	Having free time at home	Other:
5 Tsunami									
4 Large Wave									
3 Medium Wave									
2 Small Wave									
1 Calm Water									
Daily Activity →	Going to school (bus or car)	Working in a group	Going to recess or break	Eating in lunch room	Doing hard class-work	Giving a wrong answer	Doing home-work	Having free time at home	Other:

MINDFUL BREATHING—PINWHEEL

Directions: Color the pinwheel with scented markers or markers of choice. If scents are used, smell the scents on the paper to practice breathing in. Next, blow on the pinwheel to pretend to make it "spin." Practice taking deep breaths in to smell and blowing out to "spin" the pinwheel.

UNIT 3: FINDING LIFEGUARDS

INTRODUCTION

Unit 3 teaches students about the presence and importance of lifeguards and how they help us surf the waves of our feelings.

- <u>Topic 1</u> explains that lifeguards are the people who assist surfers if they need help in the water.
- <u>Topic 2</u> describes the lifeguards in our lives who can help us with challenging situations or experiences.
- <u>Topic 3</u> describes why a lifeguard is needed and how they help us surf our waves.
- <u>Topic 4</u> develops plans for those times when lifeguards are needed.
- <u>Topic 5</u> shows how we can help ourselves by using our tools, especially when there's no lifeguard.

OBJECTIVES

Students will master the following concepts:

Topic 1: What Is a Lifeguard?
- A lifeguard is a person who rescues people who are struggling when swimming or surfing.
- Lifeguards are the people in our lives that help us surf our waves safely.

Topic 2: Who Are My Lifeguards?
- Some people in our lives are helpers. It can help to know who they are and how to ask for help when we need it.
- A good lifeguard is a helper. Not all people are good lifeguards.

Topic 3: Why Do I Need a Lifeguard?
- We may need a lifeguard when we are struggling to surf our waves.
- Lifeguards help us prevent or solve surfing problems.

Topic 4: When Will Lifeguards Help Me?
- We can plan for times when we know we may need a lifeguard.
- We can ask lifeguards for help if they don't realize we are struggling.

Topic 5: What Do I Do If There Is No Lifeguard on Duty?
- We can help ourselves by being aware and knowing how to use our tools.
- We can use sensory strategies, yoga, and cognitive skills to help manage on our own.

SESSION STARTER

Begin each session with 3-5 minutes of yoga.

tree

plow

Yoga Time—Tree and Plow

Introduce the yoga poses and remind students that yoga is a type of exercise that helps your mind be calm. Poses for this set are tree and plow.

- Do the poses at the beginning of each session by showing the pictures and doing the poses with students.
- Hold each pose for a count of five. Have students take slow, deep breaths.
- Encourage students to feel the stretch in different body parts.

WAVE WATCH CHECK-IN

- Use the *Wave Watch* to have students indicate their current feelings by selecting a wave (calm water, small wave, medium wave, large wave, tsunami) or corresponding number before beginning the cognitive activities.

- Explore why students chose a certain wave, especially if they always choose the same wave. You can share examples of how your own waves change from day to day.

- You can use the *Wave Watch* at the start and end of the lesson to help students identify changes in their waves after activities.

COGNITIVE CONCEPTS

Present topics in order, selecting 1-3 activities for each session or lesson.

TOPIC 1: WHAT IS A LIFEGUARD?

1. **Lifeguards on Duty** (*Lifeguard Pictures* handout): Watch the video or look at pictures of lifeguards. Explain that a lifeguard is a person who rescues people when they get into trouble when swimming or surfing in the water. Next, have students guess how people in our lives can act as lifeguards and help us surf our feelings.

2. **Who Can Be a Lifeguard?** (*Lifeguards in My Life* handout): Show the pictures and identify the roles of the people in the pictures. Explain that these people can be lifeguards who help us navigate the waves safely when we are surfing waves of feelings. When the waves get too big or take us by surprise, we can ask for or accept help from lifeguards.

- Have students list some categories of people who might be lifeguards and then name these people: teachers, parents, therapists, counselors, coaches, childcare/babysitters, friends, and siblings.

3. **Follow the Waves** (*Wave Patterns* handout): Create wave patterns on the floor with tape or chalk. Have students choose a game card and follow the wave pattern: walk, tiptoe, stomp, hop, wiggle, crawl. Add barriers in the wave pattern and tell them what to do to avoid the barriers (e.g., hop, climb over, step to the side, crawl under, etc.).

TOPIC 2: WHO ARE MY LIFEGUARDS?

1. **Who's at the Surf Shack?** (*Lifeguard Surf Shack* handout): Ask students to name people who sometimes help them and discuss how they are helpful. Have students add these people to their *Lifeguard Surf Shack* by writing their names, drawing their picture, or pasting their photo on the wall of the shack. **Note:** Some adults automatically see themselves as lifeguards, but this may not be accurate for some students. Never assign or require a student to have a specific lifeguard. Students need to determine their own lifeguards.

2. **Who's on Duty?** (*Everyday Lifeguards* handout): Students choose 1-2 possible lifeguards who are experienced or expert surfers/helpers and tell or write what these people do to help. These are people who always provide help and support. Discuss that not everyone we like or enjoy being with will be a lifeguard or a helping person. Just as lifeguards at the pool or beach must be experts, our lifeguards need to be good at surfing the waves of their own feelings too. We all have different people who help us surf our waves depending on the situation or specific wave. For example, a friend may help you if you are feeling sad by playing with you, but they may not be able to help you when you are very tired and hungry.

3. **Lifeguards to the Rescue!** (Sensory Tactile—*Sand Rescue* handout): Students find pictures or objects in sand that represent challenging situations. Hide the *Sand Rescue* picture cards or objects in a tub of sand. Students take turns pulling out the cards or items one at time and talking about which lifeguard would help or rescue them in that situation or place.

TOPIC 3: WHY DO I NEED A LIFEGUARD?

1. **The Big Four** (*My Lifeguards and the Four Ss* handout): Explain the concept of Four Ss below, then have student complete the handout. Sometimes our waves get so big or frequent that we struggle with surfing. Everyone sometimes needs a little help from experts, and lifeguards are the people who can help when we need assistance surfing our waves.
   - **STOP problems from happening:** Lifeguards look out for dangers and warn us if something is going to make waves too big or if there are dangers in the water.
   - **SOLVE the problem together:** Lifeguards can help us consider all of the surfboard tools and decide which surfboard tools we will use.

- **SUGGEST changes for next time:** Lifeguards help by getting us materials needed for our surfboard tools, in order to help us effectively surf bigger waves in the future.
- **SUPPORT me:** Lifeguards help us feel better after big waves, so we can get out and surf again.

2. ***Rainbow Animals*** (Sensory Tactile—*Rainbow Rescue* handout): Hide the rainbow animals (paper or toy) throughout the room. Use the *Rainbow Rescue* handout to guide students on a scavenger hunt to find and rescue the animals. For more sensory motor options, animals can be under bean bags or cushions, placed in tunnels, or laid out in a designated "water" area. They can also be hidden in multiple tactile bins (rice, bean, sand, etc.) for students to rescue. For additional challenge and fun, place large paper clips on the laminated fish and use a toy fishing pole or magnet toy to rescue them.

TOPIC 4: WHEN WILL LIFEGUARDS HELP ME?

1. ***When Do I Need Help?*** (*Helpful Lifeguards* handout): Students identify times and activities on the activity sheet that may be challenging, and decide who their lifeguard(s) might be at those times. Discuss how a lifeguard being on duty means they know they are there to help if we start having difficulty or need help. Next, discuss which situations need a lifeguard on duty to help in case we face difficulty surfing our waves. Use the model below with the following examples— sports, speaking in front of a group, losing a game, taking a test, etc.

   - *Model:* "I have a very hard time surfing my waves after recess. This is a good time to know who my lifeguard might be."

2. ***How Do I Ask for Help?*** (*Asking for Help* handout): Students role play ways to ask for help. Have students watch the videos to learn how to ask for help. Use the activity sheet as a guide to have students identify challenging situations and then choose life preserver statements to role play asking for help.

TOPIC 5: WHAT DO I DO IF THERE IS NO LIFEGUARD ON DUTY?

1. ***Name That Tool!*** (*These Are the Tools for Me* handout): Students identify the surfboard tools that work best for them. Explain that there are specific tools that help us when we are struggling, even when there is not a lifeguard available to provide those tools. A lifeguard isn't always around to help when we need it. This is when we need to know which surfboard tools are the most helpful. Students will identify what tools would be helpful for them—they can write, draw, or cut and paste images to their activity sheet.

   - Surfboard tool examples may include: listening to music, talking to a friend, mindful breathing, fidget tools, taking a walk, chewing gum, etc.

2. **No Lifeguard? No Problem!** (*Finding My Calm* handout): Students select the best tools to help with difficult situations. Read through the situations on the activity sheet and ask students to recall similar situations. Review all of the tools and have students select and draw a line from the tool to the situation that tool would support them the best. Encourage students to share their own experiences related to these types of situations.

MINDFULNESS SESSION ENDER

End each session with the following mindfulness activity.

MINDFUL LISTENING

For this listening activity, use recorded ocean waves (see link in *Resources*). The goal is to have students actively focus their attention on specific sounds. Give the following directions:

> - *Sit in a comfortable position.*
> - *Listen quietly to the sound. (Play 1-5 minutes of ocean wave sounds.)*
> - *Close your eyes and focus on taking slow, deep breaths.*
> - *Listen for the crashing of the waves.*
> - *Count how many waves crash.*
> - *Can you visualize what the waves look like in your mind?*
> - *Do you hear anything else?*

Note: It is most effective to introduce these techniques when students are calm and regulated.

RESOURCES

Unit 3 Topic 1
How To Become A Lifeguard
12:00 m

Unit 3 Topic 4.1
Asking For Help
3:00 m

Unit 3 Topic 4.1
Ask For Help Song
1:00 m

Mindfulness
Ocean Waves
Play 1:00 - 5:00 m

Unit 3 Topics 1-5
Handouts

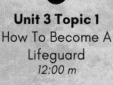

https://youtu.be/BbxfJfDKago

https://www.youtube.com/watch?v=60bj8dcFB-M

https://www.youtube.com/watch?v=Urb3GYD63og

https://youtu.be/WHPEKLQID4U

https://drive.google.com/drive/folders/1qV1Rj2tGaodiYRUGzPfLAtLlmRamhRU4?usp=drive_link

YOGA TIME

TREE POSE	PLOW POSE

Let's do **tree pose**:

- Stand tall with feet together.
- Take slow, deep breaths.
- Put your hands together at your chest.
- Put one foot on the calf of the opposite leg.
- Take one last deep breath . . . hold . . . release.

Let's do **plow pose**:

- Lie on the floor on your back with arms at your side, palms down.
- Take slow, deep breaths.
- Lift your legs and point your toes at the ceiling.
- Bend at the waist and pull your legs over your head until your toes touch the floor.
- Take one last deep breath . . . hold . . . release.

LIFEGUARD PICTURES

109

LIFEGUARDS IN MY LIFE

Friend

Coach

Grandparents

Sitter

Brother or Sister

Therapist

Parents

Teacher

WAVE PATTERNS

Directions: Cut the cards apart. Students will choose a card and follow the wave pattern on the floor using the action on the card. Other students will give surfers directions to avoid the barriers (e.g., hop, climb over, step to the side, crawl under, etc.).

tiptoe

hop

walk

wiggle

stomp

crawl

LIFEGUARD SURF SHACK

Directions: Who are your lifeguards? Put their names or pictures in the boxes on the lifeguard shack.

EVERYDAY LIFEGUARDS

Directions: Write the names of 1–2 people who help you in different places or environments, then discuss what they do to help you in these environments.

HOME

_____

_____

SCHOOL

_____

_____

ACTIVITIES & SPORTS

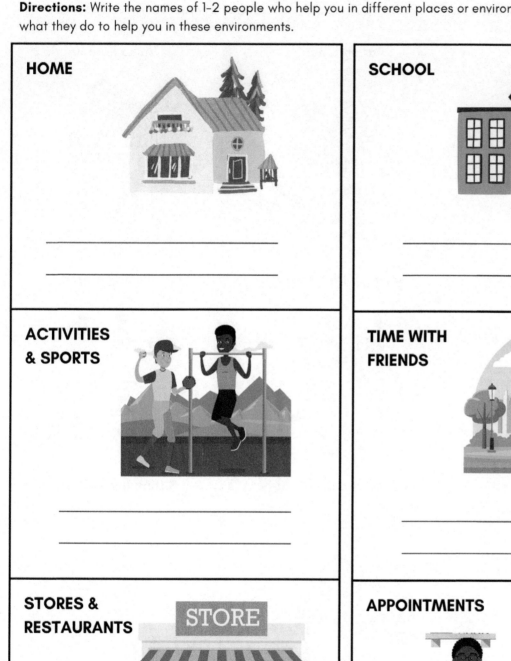

_____

_____

TIME WITH FRIENDS

_____

_____

STORES & RESTAURANTS

_____

_____

APPOINTMENTS

_____

_____

SAND RESCUE

Directions: Cut out cards, or use objects to represent situations (e.g., pencil for homework; small figure for too many people; small ball for recess; etc.). Bury cards in sand, then pull out pictures one at time and talk about which of your lifeguards would help or rescue you in that situation or place. Note: Laminate cards to make more durable.

Riding the bus 	**Eating lunch** 	**Doing homework** 
Working in a group 	**Talking with a friend** 	**Losing a game** 
Wearing scratchy clothes 	**Feeling tired and hungry** 	**Sitting in a bright room** 
Going to the doctor 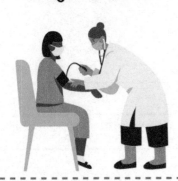	**Going to a crowded area** 	**Going to a noisy place** 

MY LIFEGUARDS AND THE FOUR Ss

Directions: Sometimes our waves get so big or frequent that we struggle with surfing. Our lifeguards can help by using the Four Ss. Select one of the Four Ss (Stop, Solve, Suggest, Support) that a lifeguard might provide for each situation in the beach scene and write it in the corresponding box. Remember, there is no right or wrong answer. Different things work for different people.

I'm very nervous, and I am afraid
I can't do this without help.

I'm having a big wave and have
to go do something really hard.

I had a tsunami and I
feel terrible now.

I'm angry and tense. I don't know what
tool to use to help me calm down.

I'm really tired, and this work is hard.

Are these waves going
to be too big for me to surf?

I just had a big argument with my
friend and want to cry and get away.

Last time I did this I had a tsunami—
is it safe to go in the water?

<u>STOP</u> problems from happening	<u>SOLVE</u> the problem together	<u>SUGGEST</u> changes for next time	<u>SUPPORT</u> me

© Tracey DeMaria, Autism Moving Forward

RAINBOW RESCUE

MATERIALS

- **Rainbow Ocean Animals:*** Make three or more copies, cut, and laminate (if possible) ocean animals below.
- **Tactile Bins:** Bins filled with rice, beans, sand, etc.
- **Ocean Activity Area:** Designate an area and use items such as a tunnel, carpet squares, tape, cushions, bean bags, etc.

May substitute with plush or plastic toy ocean animals.

DIRECTIONS

1. **Make the *Ocean Activity Area:*** Use visual boundaries for the activity area and provide mats, cushions, bean bags, bowls, boxes, etc. to hide the animals.
2. **Scavenger Hunt:** Show students the ocean animals they are to find. Demonstrate finding 1-2 then have students find and rescue at least 6-8 rainbow ocean animals.
3. **Discussion:** Talk to students about being lifeguards as they rescue the animals. Have students talk about a time they had help from a lifeguard.

RAINBOW OCEAN ANIMALS

HELPFUL LIFEGUARDS

Directions: Circle the situations that can cause your waves to get big, then name a lifeguard who will give you support to get back to calm waters. Review the list of lifeguards on your *Lifeguard Surf Shack*, if needed.

Situations	Lifeguard
1. Coming back to class after my favorite activity (recess, library, gym, lunch, etc.).	
2. I have to work with someone in class who I don't know.	
3. There is a change in my schedule.	
4. We have an assembly at school that will be noisy and crowded.	
5. I want to play with someone, but I don't know how to ask.	
6. I don't feel well . . . . I am tired. I am hungry. Something hurts.	
7. Something happened at home that is upsetting me.	
8. I am in trouble, and I am mad about it.	
9. I am in a grumpy mood today, and I want to feel better.	
10. I am going to miss something I really want to do.	

ASKING FOR HELP page 1

Directions: Role play asking lifeguards for help. Read all of the wave situations below and share similar experiences of your own. Next, choose a life preserver (next page) and role play asking for help by using one of the life preserver statements or actions. Remember, there are no right or wrong answers. Different things work for different people. Note: Your instructor may read the statements out loud to you, if needed.

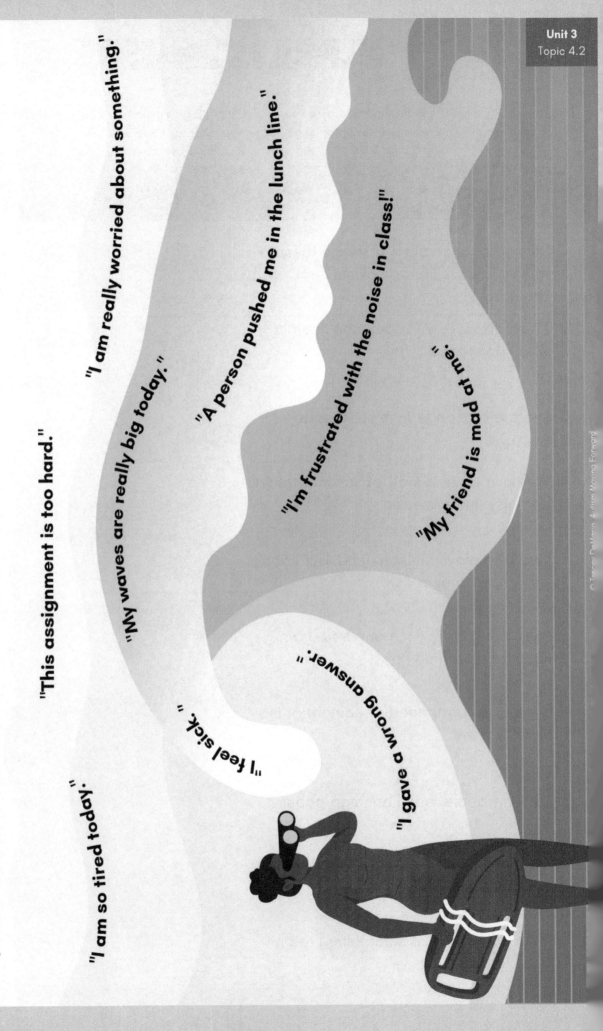

"I am really worried about something."

"A person pushed me in the lunch line."

"I'm frustrated with the noise in class!"

"My friend is mad at me."

"This assignment is too hard."

"My waves are really big today."

"I gave a wrong answer."

"I feel sick."

"I am so tired today."

118

ASKING FOR HELP page 2

Directions: Choose a life preserver and role play asking for help, using one of the life preserver statements or actions.
Note: Your instructor may read the statements out loud to you, if needed. All approximations of any spoken words or gestured should be honored.

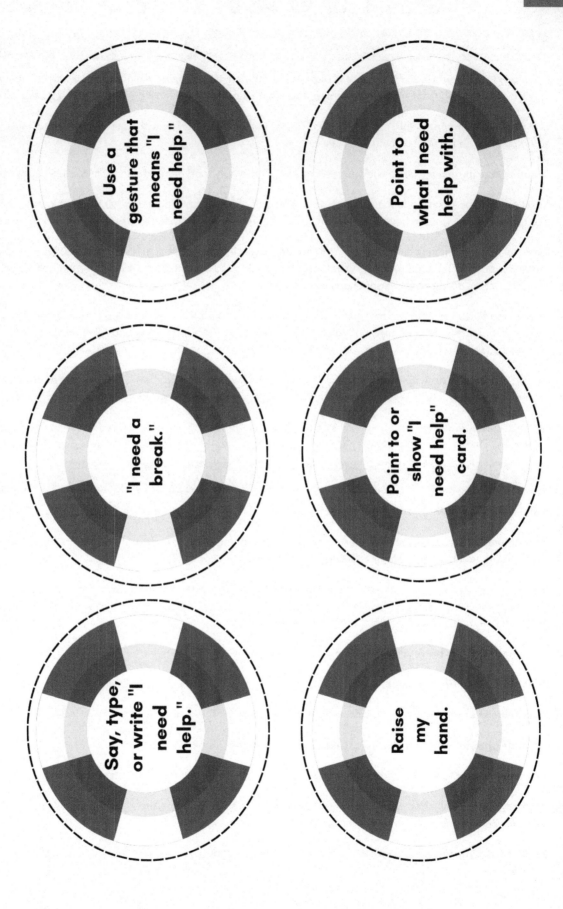

Use a gesture that means "I need help."

"I need a break."

Say, type, or write "I need help."

Point to what I need help with.

Point to or show "I need help" card.

Raise my hand.

My Body Can Surf the Waves

Do heavy muscle work: Jump, crash, climb, push, pull, stretch, do yoga, use weighted items, deep pressure massage, head/hand/arm/leg/foot squeezes, or compression clothing. This is the most powerful tool for surfing all waves!

Get your body moving: Walk, run, swing, skip, dance, spin, rock on foot or in chair, bounce or roll on yoga ball, ride bike/scooter, stand on balance board, do obstacle courses.

Mouth: Crunchy/chewy foods, chew tubes/necklaces, safe non-food items to chew, sour/spicy tastes for intensity.

Ears: Noise-canceling headphones to decrease background noise; calming music (60 beats/minute), white noise to help with background noise, Tibetan bowl or chime, preferred music to help with mood/distraction.

Eyes: Avoid bright, florescent, and flashing lights; calm by using dim, muted, and steady lights. Light or spinning toys (color-changing, flashlights), sand toys, toys with falling or spilling (sand from hand into bin, water through funnel). Clutter-free work area, few visual distractions, wear sunglasses outside and in.

Touch and feel: Play dough, slime, goo, sand, putty, moon sand, kinetic sand, shaving cream, lotion. Pops-its, stress balls, squishy items, water tubes, soft plush toys, and fabric. Dry vs. wet (chalk/sand/flour on hands versus sticky, slimy, or mushy items). Hot vs. cold (ice packs, warm packs).

Smell: Calming scents (lavender, vanilla) vs. more alerting scents (mint, orange), but individual preferences matter most! Use natural items if possible—chemicals can be too strong/unhealthy. Limit or avoid fragrances and perfumes.

Internal sensations: Are you hungry, thirsty? Tired, awake? Breathing slow, fast? Need to use the bathroom? Need it more frequently? Does your head feel buzzy, foggy? In pain, sick? Get enough sleep, drink fluids, and eat healthy foods.

Body Tools

I've Got Surfing on the Brain

Have a conversation: Talk to a friend or someone else about how you are feeling or what is on your mind.

Storytelling: Write or tell a story, write in a journal, tell someone about your favorite game or subject, draw a picture, make a video. If you are uncomfortable, use writing or typing tools.

Screen time: Too much unstructured screen time can be overstimulating or even addictive. You can use screen time to redirect your brain with video games, tablets, computer. Be careful not to watch something that you know can upset you or be overstimulating. Avoid screen time for an hour before bedtime.

Read or listen to a book you enjoy: Books, magazines, comic books.

Puzzles or other brain games: Sudoku, word searches, cryptograms, mazes, crosswords, jigsaw puzzles.

Mindfulness tools: Do mindful breathing, watch a mindfulness video, do a mindfulness activity.

Animals or pets: Cuddle, exercise, or feed your own or a friend's pet.

Get organized: Make a list of goals, activities, or steps, being sure to cross them off when done.

Memory work: Think about your favorite memories—places, special events, times with friends: Who was there? What did it look like? Do you remember noises or smells? Did you eat something yummy?

Problem solving: Review a problem you are having, checking your memories for fact vs. fiction. Do this on your own or ask adult for help.

Be creative or learn something new: Do art projects or crafts, sing a song, try to remember steps to a dance. Coloring books, mandalas, doodling with markers. Read about a new interest or idea. Memorize a poem or song.

Brain Tools

THESE ARE THE TOOLS FOR ME

Directions: Review the *Surfboard Tools* chart. Identify the tools that work best for you, especially when you may not have a lifeguard nearby to help. Write, draw, or cut out and paste images onto the surfboards. Examples: listening to music, talking to a friend, mindful breathing, fidget tools, taking a walk, chewing gum, etc.

Heavy Muscle Work: Jump or Stretch!

FINDING MY CALM

Directions: Read the following list of situations, then choose a tool from the list that will help you get back to calm waters. Draw a line from the situation to the tool that will help you the most.

SITUATION		TOOL
I feel very tired.	•	Headphones
I am hungry.	•	Sunglasses
I am very cold.	•	Blanket, jacket
I am very hot.	•	Comfy clothes
It is very noisy.	•	Food
I am very thirsty.	•	Fidget
I am overwhelmed.	•	Break time
It is too crowded.	•	Fan, ice pack
The light is too bright.	•	Rest time
My clothes are scratchy and tight.	•	Get a drink

UNIT 4: WATCH OUT FOR SHARKS

INTRODUCTION

Unit 4 teaches students that sharks are the challenges we face in our lives that can be dangerous if we are not careful.

- <u>Topic 1</u> describes how challenges are like sharks in the water.
- <u>Topic 2</u> explains how to notice or predict sharks in the water.
- <u>Topic 3</u> helps us identify our sharks, figure out how big they are, and learn what causes them.
- <u>Topic 4</u> explains that we all have sharks but can learn to deal with them.
- <u>Topic 5</u> is about finding ways to deal with sharks when we are surfing our waves.

OBJECTIVES

Students will master the following concepts:

Topic 1: What Is a Shark?
- Challenges are like sharks: They make it difficult to surf the waves of daily life.
- We can be prepared for sharks by noticing warning signs, getting help and support, or avoiding them.

Topic 2: How Do I Know When There Are Sharks in the Water?
- We can learn how to identify sharks and predict when they might show up.
- We can learn to identify the situations, people, and environments that might be the sharks that make surfing our feelings more difficult.

Topic 3: What Are My Sharks?
- We can learn what our sharks might be and how to be aware of the dangers they present.
- We can identify and rate the intensity and size of our sharks or triggers.

Topic 4: Why Are There Sharks in the Water?
- Sharks and challenges are a regular part of life, but we can learn to see them coming.
- We may have thoughts and beliefs that make sharks more likely.

Topic 5: What Do I Do if I See a Shark?
- We can use our Body and Brain Surfboard Tools as coping skills for fending off sharks.
- There are techniques we can use for coping with dangerous sharks, big waves, and tsunamis.

SESSION STARTER

Begin each session with 3–5 minutes of yoga.

triangle

warrior

Yoga Time—Triangle and Warrior

Introduce the yoga poses and remind students that yoga is a type of exercise that helps your mind be calm. Poses for this unit are triangle and warrior.

- Do the poses at the beginning of each session by showing the pictures and doing the poses with students.
- Hold each pose for a count of five. Have students take slow, deep breaths.
- Encourage students to feel the stretch in different body parts.

WAVE WATCH CHECK-IN

- Use the *Wave Watch* to have students indicate their current feelings by selecting a wave (calm water, small wave, medium wave, large wave, tsunami) or corresponding number before beginning the cognitive activities.

- Explore why students chose a certain wave, especially if they always choose the same wave. You can share examples of how your own waves change from day to day.

- You can use the *Wave Watch* at the start and end of the lesson to help students identify changes in their waves after activities.

COGNITIVE CONCEPTS

Present topics in order, selecting 1–3 activities for each session or lesson.

TOPIC 1: WHAT IS A SHARK?

1. ***Sharks, Sharks, and More Sharks!*** (*Shark Pictures* handout): Introduce sharks by showing pictures and/or videos of sharks (only informational, not scary—see links in *Resources*). Talk about how we all have problems in our lives that get in our way and may be frustrating and stressful. These problems are like sharks in the water and can be dangerous when we are surfing our waves. We can use our surfing tools to avoid sharks and be safe in the water.

2. ***Sharks Ahead!*** (*Surprise Sharks* handout): Students complete the activity sheet to identify surprise sharks, or triggers, as challenges that show up when we least expect them and cause stress at school and at home. Read through the list and ask students to identify sharks or things that have caused (or might cause) unexpected stress in their lives. Have students mark 3–4 and

then ask them to give more detail by asking questions about a specific shark or trigger:

- "Tell me about a time when you were stressed because . . . (e.g., teacher yelled)?"
- "What happened when you were feeling . . . (e.g., so hungry)?"
- "How did you feel when . . . (e.g., peer looked at you)?"

3. *Fun With Sharks* (Sensory Tactile): Help students understand that sharks can be scary until you know how to deal with them. Let students create their own sharks out of play dough. They can make faces on their sharks using googly eyes and pipe cleaners. Make a tabletop into an "ocean" and have kids move their sharks around. Allow free play with play dough for more sensory input.

TOPIC 2: HOW DO I KNOW THERE ARE SHARKS IN THE WATER?

1. *Danger Zone—Sharks in the Water* (*Dangerous Sharks* handout): Students complete the activity sheet to identify triggers or sharks, including specific situations, people, and environments that make surfing the waves of our feelings difficult.

2. *It's a Shark!* (Sensory Tactile—*My Shark* handout): Students use a tactile medium (e.g., Wiki Stix, clay, puffy glue, yarn, or bits of crumpled tissue paper, etc.) and the *My Shark* printable to create their own shark.

3. *Shark Patrol* (Sensory Visual Motor—*Spot the Shark* handout): Students will use small flashlights or pen lights to spot the shark among different sea animals. Attach the *Spot the Shark* handout to the wall. Have students take turns standing a few feet away. Students will aim the flashlight at the page, moving from left to right and going from top to bottom (as when we read) while saying the name of each sea animal until they find sharks. Each time they find a shark, the student will yell "Shark!"

- Optional activity: Place larger pictures of sharks around a dimly lit activity area and have students spot the sharks with the flashlight.

TOPIC 3: WHAT ARE MY SHARKS?

1. *Avoid the Shark!* (Sensory Motor—*Shark Attack Game* handout; *Shark Attack Cards* handout): Students play the game by moving between safe areas to avoid sharks in the water. Set up game area with a path of safe areas and trigger spots (see *Shark Attack Game* handout). For safe areas, use hula hoops, carpet squares, plastic spots, or tape on the floor. Prepare *Shark Attack Cards* by labeling and cutting apart cards and placing them between safe areas. Be sure the safe areas are close enough that students can jump from place to place but far enough to be challenging.

2. *Mapping the Waters for Sharks* (*Shark Mapping* handout): Students label the sharks on the *Shark Mapping* handout. Students label bigger sharks with more challenging situations and smaller sharks with easier-to-handle situations.

3. **Find the Sharks** (Sensory Tactile—*Shark Foam Slime* handout): Students experience sensory input while exploring how to move their hands in slime* to find and remove sharks. Make slime using the directions sheet, add sharks (sharks can be any small item, e.g., mini clothespins, blocks, erasers, plastic counters, etc.), and have students explore and remove any sharks they find.

   *May use pre-made slime or a bin of rice or beans.

TOPIC 4: WHY ARE THERE SHARKS IN THE WATER?

1. **Sharks Are a Part of Life** (*Accepting the Sharks* handout): Explain that sharks and challenges are an everyday part of life that we can learn to cope with. Read the situations on the handout and have students describe and/or write emotion(s) they might experience in these situations. Take it further and have students compare the situations to their own lives and/or ask students to name a time they had a similar emotion.

2. **Staying Safe** (Sensory Motor): Use movement and balance toys such as yoga balls, swings, scooters, balance beams, playground climbing equipment, etc. Have students use their bodies to explore these items. Talk about caution and safety. For example, what happens if you go too fast or don't watch where you are going? Ask if they have ever been hurt or know of someone else who was hurt when playing, (a skinned knee, bump or bruise, etc.). It is important to think about how to be safe when we play because if we are not safe with our bodies, we can get hurt.

3. **Starfish Breathing** (Sensory Tactile—*Starfish Breathing Buddy* handout): Hold up one hand in a starfish position with fingers spread apart and demonstrate the following movement: Slowly and softly trace up and down each finger with the other hand, focusing on regular breathing at the same time. Trace up the finger—inhale. Trace down the finger—exhale. Repeat and have students follow along with their own hands.
   - For more fun, follow the directions on the *Starfish Breathing Buddy* activity sheet. Students make their own salt dough starfish. Once students are familiar with the simple five-finger starfish breathing, they can practice starfish breathing using their own decorated starfish.

TOPIC 5: WHAT DO I DO IF I SEE A SHARK?

1. **Outsurf Those Sharks!** (*Surfboards and Sharks* handout): Students complete the handout by coming up with a list of at least five of their specific sharks plus five surfboard tools that they can use to help outsurf the sharks or avoid them completely.

2. **Use Your Five Senses** (*My Five Senses* handout): Have students look around their space and think of **five** things they can see, **four** things they can feel, **three** things they can hear, **two** things they can smell, and **one** thing they can taste. If they say they cannot find enough items of any sense, they can try to remember what something looked like, felt like, sounded like, etc.

MINDFULNESS SESSION ENDER

End each session with the following mindfulness activity.

MINDFULNESS ACTIVITY

Mindful Stretching

Show students jellyfish and octopus visuals (see *Mindful Sea Stretching* handout) and talk about how they both use their tentacles to move around by stretching and relaxing.

> *We are going to pretend we are like an octopus or jellyfish. Lie down in a comfortable position with space for your arms and legs to stretch.*
>
> - *Our arms and legs are our tentacles. Let's practice stretching and relaxing them.*
> - *Start by stretching your arms and hands up above your head, and legs and feet straight out below you.*
> - *Stretch your muscles as far as you can, and pay attention to how the muscles in your arms, hands, legs, and feet feel as they stretch. Do you feel the stretch and pull of muscles anywhere else? How about your back or belly?*
> - *Without changing position, relax all the muscles in your arms and legs. Pay attention to how the muscles in your arms, hands, legs, and feet feel. Do they tingle? Are they loose?*

Repeat this stretching and relaxing of your tentacles at least three times, paying attention to how the muscles feel while stretching then relaxing.

RESOURCES

 Unit 4 Topic 1
All About Sharks for Kids
8:00 m

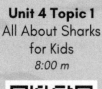

https://www.youtube.com/watch?v=kl9qJMpoYqs

 Unit 4 Topic 1
Cool Facts About Sharks
2:00 m

https://youtu.be/WzKs948SEZ8

 Unit 4 Topic 1
Sharks 101
5:00 m

https://youtu.be/4HGNqFdaD34

 Unit 4 Topics 1–5
Handouts

https://drive.google.com/drive/folders/1njoht6pJmki01ZPB1-5zmBEwnjaWeglQ?usp=drive_link

YOGA TIME

TRIANGLE POSE

WARRIOR POSE

Let's do **triangle pose**:
- Stand with feet together and hands at your side.
- Take slow deep breaths.
- Jump your feet apart.
- Turn your right foot out and your left foot forward.
- Raise and stretch your arms out.
- Bend to the right until your hand touches your ankle.
- Take one last deep breath . . . hold . . . release.

Let's do **warrior pose**:
- Stand with feet together and hands at your side.
- Take slow deep breaths.
- Jump your feet apart.
- Turn your right foot in and your left foot forward.
- Raise and stretch your arms out.
- Turn your head to the left and bend your left knee.
- Take one last deep breath . . . hold . . . release.

SHARK PICTURES

SURPRISE SHARKS

Directions: Identify several sharks or triggers that have caused (or might cause) unexpected stress in your life. Mark 3-4 then answer questions to give more detail about a specific shark or trigger.

So TIRED

So HUNGRY

So THIRSTY

Too LOUD

Too CROWDED

Too DIFFICULT

SCARED me

IGNORED me

PUSHED me

YELLED at me

LOOKED at me

TALKED to me

130

© Tracey DeMaria, Autism Moving Forward

DANGEROUS SHARKS

Directions: Some people, places, experiences, or feelings may be triggers that are like sharks in the ocean—making it hard to surf the waves of everyday life. Check off all of the shark triggers in your life and add any details, including names of people, places, and other information that will help you identify shark triggers. Then, list your biggest shark triggers.

Possible Triggers

People
- [ ] adult at school
- [ ] peer at school
- [ ] family member
- [ ] other person

Time of Day
- [ ] waking up
- [ ] going to school
- [ ] after school
- [ ] mealtime
- [ ] bedtime

Body Feelings
- [ ] loud noises
- [ ] bright lights
- [ ] too many people
- [ ] strong smells
- [ ] hungry or thirsty
- [ ] hot or cold
- [ ] tired or sick

Places
- [ ] school
- [ ] home
- [ ] doctor's office
- [ ] restaurants
- [ ] stores
- [ ] parties
- [ ] assemblies

Experiences
- [ ] speaking in class
- [ ] losing a privilege
- [ ] doing homework
- [ ] taking a test
- [ ] gym class
- [ ] working in a group
- [ ] hanging out with friends

List your biggest triggers from these lists:
- [ ] _____
- [ ] _____
- [ ] _____
- [ ] _____
- [ ] _____

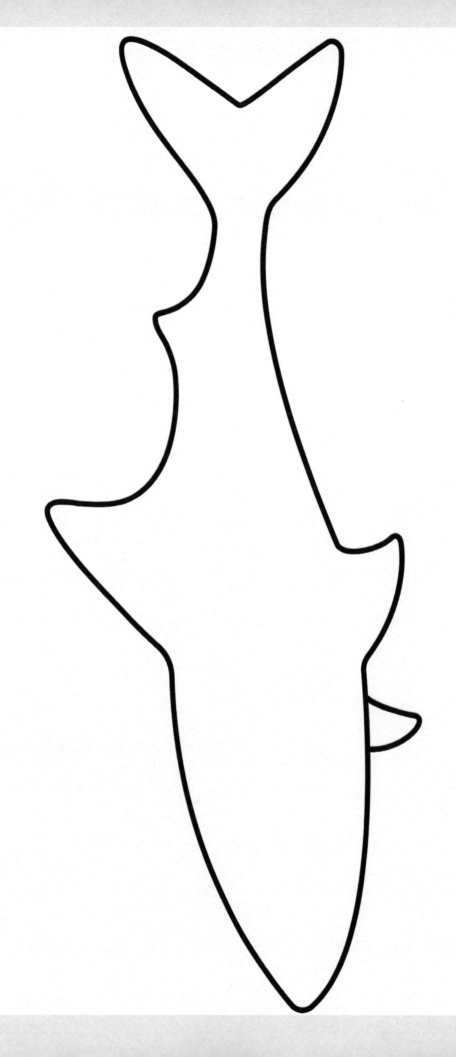

MY SHARK

SPOT THE SHARK

Directions: Use a flashlight to spot the shark among different sea animals. Attach the handout to the wall. Standing a few feet away, aim the flashlight at the page, moving from left to right and going from top to bottom (as when we read) while saying the name of each sea animal until you find sharks. Each time you find a shark, yell "Shark!"

SHARK ATTACK GAME

Instructor directions: Arrange the room with safe spaces ⬭ and trigger spots. 🦈 For safe areas use hula hoops, carpet squares, plastic spots, or tape on the floor. Scatter *Shark Attack Cards* between safe areas. (Make additional *Shark Attack Cards*, as needed.) Be sure the spaces are close enough that students can jump from place to place, but not close enough that they can easily walk. (See below for sample game path.)

Students play the game by moving between safe areas to avoid sharks in the water. As students pass the trigger spots, talk about each trigger and some tools that might help the student pass that trigger successfully.

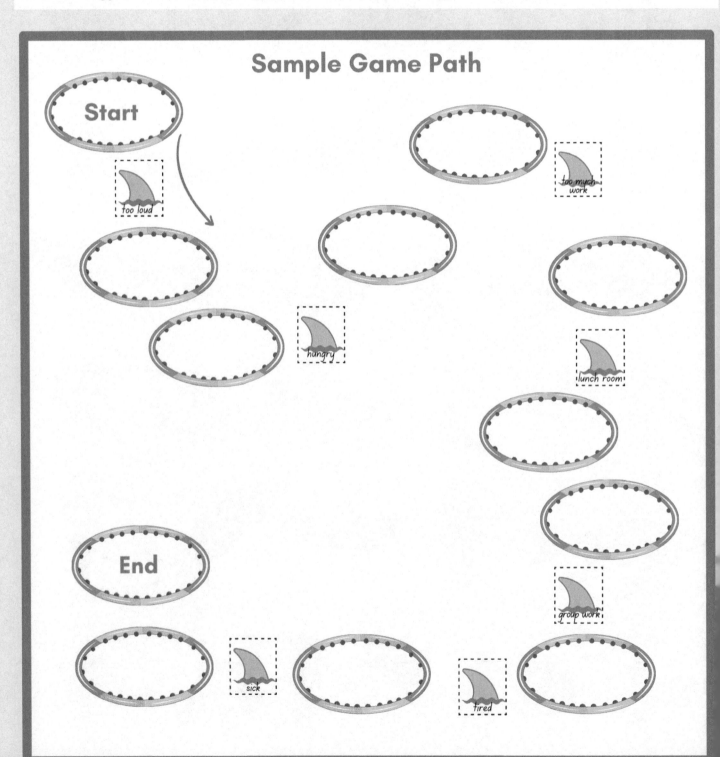

Sample Game Path

SHARK ATTACK CARDS

Directions: Referring to the list from the *Danger Zone: Sharks in the Water* activity (Topic 2.1), cut apart the cards and place one card in each of the "trigger spots" (areas to avoid) in the game area. Print and use as many sets of cards as needed.

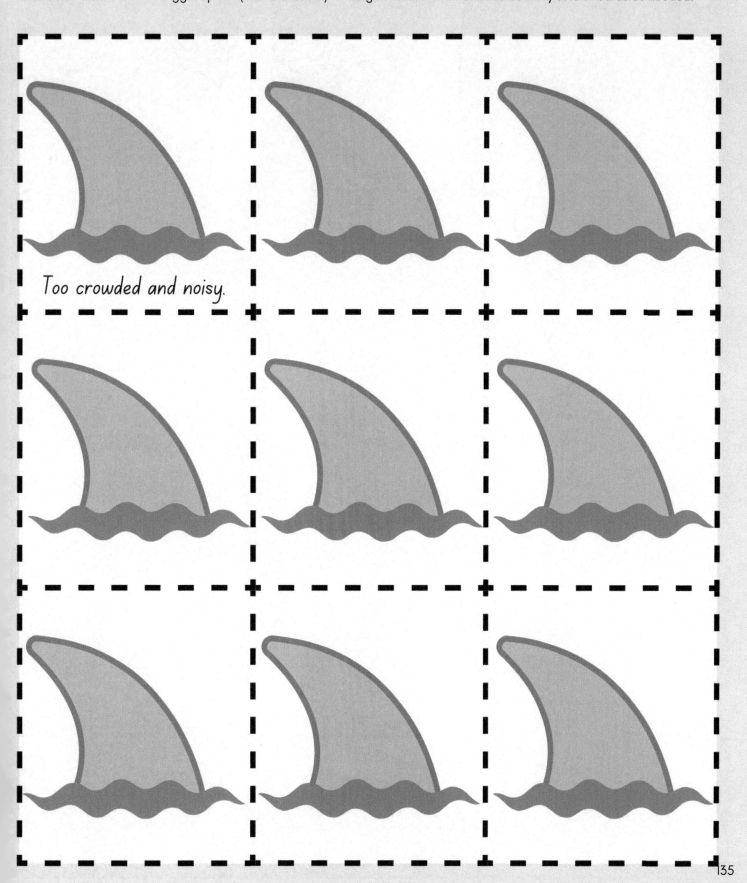

Too crowded and noisy.

SHARK MAPPING

Directions: Pick your top nine sharks and map them on the diagram below by labeling the sharks. Remember, sharks represent triggers or danger in the water for a surfer. Use bigger sharks for the most difficult situations or experiences and smaller sharks for ones that are less difficult.

SHARK FOAM SLIME

MATERIALS

- 1 (5 oz.) bottle clear glue
- ½ cup of liquid starch
- ½ cup of warm water
- 1 cup white or blue foam beads/foam balls/mini styrofoam polystyrene balls
- Measuring cups
- Mixing bowl
- Spoon
- Mini plastic toy sharks (or other small items, e.g., mini clothespins or paperclips)
- Storage container or bag

DIRECTIONS

1. Pour full contents of glue into mixing bowl.
2. Add the water and stir.
3. Slowly add the liquid starch and stir—it should quickly become slime consistency.
4. Stir in one cup of foam balls.
5. Knead slime with hands until desired consistency.
6. Provide student with mini toy plastic sharks (or other small items) to embed in the slime.

SUGGESTED QUESTIONS

For the *Find the Sharks* activity, make the *Shark Foam Slime** and add sharks (use small toy sharks or any small items to symbolize sharks such as plastic counters, mini clothespins, erasers, etc.) to the slime and encourage students to move their hands through the slime to find and remove the sharks. Have students talk about their sharks or triggers by answer the following questions:

1. What are the sharks in your life?
2. What do you do when you get too close to a shark?
3. Name some ways you avoid your shark triggers.
4. Name some tools you use to help with shark triggers.

*Instead of using *Shark Foam Slime*, you can use pre-made slime or fill a bin with rice or beans, add the sharks, and follow the activity directions above.

ACCEPTING THE SHARKS

Directions: Read the shark triggers below and brainstorm with your instructor about different emotions that might be experienced in these situations. Look at the **Triggers** and **Emotions** examples at the bottom of the page for ideas, then write or dictate answers in the **Surfer Emotion** column. Take it further and compare the situations to your own experiences and then name a time you had a similar emotion.

Shark Trigger Situation	Surfer Emotion
1. I have to stop or am not allowed to do something I want to do: play a game, play outside, take a break, screen time, etc.	
2. My body feelings are intense, big, and uncomfortable: very hot, really hungry, very noisy, clothes are extremely tight or scratchy, etc.	
3. I made a mistake: wrong answer on a test or assignment, a drawing doesn't look right, I accidentally broke a rule, etc.	
4. I have to be somewhere or do something I don't want to do: going inside from recess, going to the doctor, doing my classwork, working in a group, etc.	
5. Something special or important to me is broken or lost: favorite object, game, collection, book, etc.	

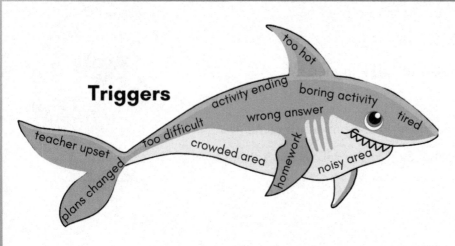

Triggers

too hot · activity ending · boring activity · wrong answer · tired · teacher upset · too difficult · crowded area · homework · noisy area · plans changed

Emotions

anxious · scared · nervous · angry · sorry · frustrated · sad

© Tracey DeMaria, Autism Moving Forward

STARFISH BREATHING BUDDY

This supplemental activity can be dane across multiple days.

MATERIALS

Ingredients for salt dough:
- 1 cup salt
- 1 cup water
- 2 cups flour

Supplies:
- Non-toxic paints
- Paintbrushes
- Clear sealant (for longer-lasting starfish, coat them with clear sealant)

DIRECTIONS

No-Bake Salt Dough Starfish Recipe

1. Mix salt, water, and flour in a bowl until dough is smooth.
2. Roll the dough to about 8mm thickness.
3. Shape the dough into a starfish. Start with a ball of dough and gently pull out five arms evenly spaced around the center.
4. Place the starfish shapes on a microwave-safe plate.
5. Microwave on low heat for 1-2 minutes (or bake for 2-3 hours at the lowest heat until hard and dry).
6. Let the starfish cool and harden.
7. Paint the starfish using non-toxic paints.
8. Allow them to dry.

DIRECTED PRACTICE

To practice starfish breathing, have students sit in a comfortable position holding their starfish and give the following directions:

- *Find an arm on your starfish. Very slowly follow the arm up while breathing in, then very slowly follow the arm down while breathing out.*
- *Repeat with a second arm—very slowly following the arm up and breathing in, then very slowly breathe out while following the arm down.*
- *Repeat for arms three, four, and five.*

Encourage students to think about how the starfish feels in their hands while they are starfish breathing, watching their hands and starfish move up and down as they breathe.

SURFBOARDS AND SHARKS

Directions: Make a list of at least five of your sharks. Then think about previous lessons and come up with a surfboard tool for each shark so you can outsurf them, or avoid them completely.

SHARKS 	SURFBOARD TOOLS
Coming into class after lunch or outside time.	Get a drink and do wave breathing exercise.

Surfboard Tools

Drink water
Play a game
Eat a snack
Rest
Stretch
Read a book
Move my body
Breathing exercises

Be alone
Turn off lights
Take a break
Quiet time
Go for a walk
Play with fidgets
Use slime or sand

Blow bubbles
Listen to music
Use play dough
Ask for help

MY FIVE SENSES

Directions: Look around your space and name **five** things you can see, **four** things you can feel, **three** things you can hear, **two** things you can smell (or remember a smell), and **one** thing you can taste (or remember a taste).

5 Things you can see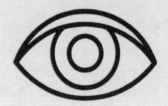

4 Things you can feel

3 Things you can hear

2 Things you can smell

1 Thing you can taste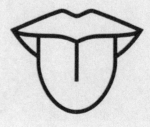

MINDFUL SEA STRETCHING

> *We are going to pretend we are an octopus or a jellyfish. Lie down in a comfortable position with space to stretch out your arms and legs.*
>
> - *Our arms and legs are like tentacles and we will practice stretching and relaxing them.*
> - *Start by stretching your arms and hands up above your head, and your legs and feet straight out below you.*
> - *Stretch your muscles as far as you can, paying attention to how the muscles in your arms, hands, legs, and feet feel as they stretch. Do you feel the stretch and pull of muscles anywhere else? How about your back and belly?*
> - *Without changing position, relax all the muscles in your arms and legs. Pay attention to how the muscles in your arms, hands, legs, and feet feel now. Do they tingle? Are they loose?*

UNIT 5: SURVIVING THE STORM

INTRODUCTION

Unit 5 teaches students about storms—times when surfing gets even more challenging. Students will practice using their surfboard tools and skills to problem solve and advocate for themselves.

- <u>Topic 1</u> describes how storms can cause our waves to be bigger and more frequent.
- <u>Topic 2</u> helps us plan for storms and times when waves get bigger and more intense.
- <u>Topic 3</u> is about finding ways to understand our behavior as we deal with storms.
- <u>Topic 4</u> explains how we can use our skills to ride out big storms and how to let others know what we need.
- <u>Topic 5</u> helps us reflect on how we surf our waves and how to surf successfully in the future.

OBJECTIVES

Students will master the following concepts:

Topic 1: What Are Storms?
- Storms are times when weather gets bad and causes waves to be bigger and more frequent.
- We all experience storms—times when many stressful or challenging situations occur simultaneously.

Topic 2: How Can I Plan for Storms?
- We can predict storms that may impact our waves.
- Sometimes we aren't aware a storm is coming until we are in the middle of it.

Topic 3: What Can I Do During a Storm?
- We can learn to understand how our behavior can affect our storms.
- We can figure out ways to be more regulated as storms are approaching.

Topic 4: How Do I Ride Out the Storm?
- We all need ways to get through stormy weather that can create tsunamis and big waves.
- We can take charge of our own surfing tools and let people around us know what we need.

Topic 5: How Do I Come Back to the Beach?
- After storms have passed, we can reflect on how we surf our daily waves, and we can make plans for future surfing.
- We can use what we've learned to surf our waves with more confidence in the future.

SESSION STARTER

Begin each session with 3-5 minutes of yoga.

Yoga Time—Boat and Camel

Introduce the yoga poses and remind students that yoga is a type of exercise that helps your mind be calm. Poses for this unit are boat and camel.

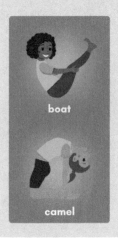

- Do the poses at the beginning of each session by showing the pictures and doing the poses with students.
- Hold each pose for a count of five. Have students take slow, deep breaths.
- Encourage students to feel the stretch in different body parts.

WAVE WATCH CHECK-IN

- Use the *Wave Watch* to have students indicate their current feelings by selecting a wave (calm water, small wave, medium wave, large wave, tsunami) or corresponding number before beginning the cognitive activities.
- Explore why students chose a certain wave, especially if they always choose the same wave. You can share examples of how your own waves change from day to day.
- You can use the *Wave Watch* at the start and end of the lesson to help students identify changes in their waves after activities.

COGNITIVE CONCEPTS

Present topics in order, selecting 1-3 activities for each session or lesson.

TOPIC 1: WHAT ARE STORMS?

1. ***How Do Storms Impact Waves?*** (*Stormy Waves* handout): Introduce the concept by showing the wave pictures and videos of storms. Guide students to identify how storms can be very strong and can vary in severity (thunderstorms vs. hurricanes). Storms can sometimes cause our waves to be bigger and closer together.

2. ***What's the Forecast?*** (*Storm Forecast* handout): Students will identify 3-5 challenging situations and compare them to different storms (e.g., rainstorms, thunderstorms, hurricanes, etc.). Students can learn to predict emotional storms that may cause big waves. When students know a storm is coming, they can have their surfing tools ready. Just as we carry umbrellas when rain is coming, students can have their tools and strategies ready when emotional storms are looming.

3. ***Storms of Glitter*** (Sensory—*Glitter Bottle* handout): Students make a glitter storm out of a plastic water bottle, using water, glitter, a small funnel, and duct tape. Add water to the bottle then small scoops of glitter. Finally, seal the bottle with duct tape. Students shake and turn the glitter bottle to show how waves look during a storm. When movement stops, the glitter settles—just as storms eventually blow over and intense waves settle down.

Note: The glitter bottle is also used for the mindfulness activity in this unit.

TOPIC 2: HOW CAN I PLAN FOR STORMS?

1. ***Beach Bag Emergency Kit*** (*My Emergency Kit* handout): Students each create their own emergency kit by writing or drawing items representing skills and items they will need when faced with big waves (e.g., *Breathe With the Wave* card, sensory fidgets, movement, activities, etc.). Display each student's *Emergency Kit* asa reminder to practice their surfing skills for waves caused by storms.

2. ***Emergency! Make a Plan*** (*Emergency Plan* handout): Explain that being prepared is the best way to survive an emotional storm while minimizing any damage. Making an emergency plan involves learning how to identify potential storms and preparing for larger waves or bigger feelings by having readily accessible tools and strategies. When a plan is in place, the next big storm will be more manageable.

3. ***Watch Out for Storm Clouds*** (Sensory Tactile—*Storm Clouds and Storm Scripts* handout): Lead a discussion using the *Storm Scripts* portion of the handout while the students are working on their project—sometimes it is easier to discuss feelings when engaged in a fun activity. The *Storm Scripts* handout describes several emotional storm situations with question prompts to get students thinking as they make a 3-D storm picture out of materials such as cotton balls, tissue paper, and plastic objects.

TOPIC 3: WHAT DO I DO DURING A STORM?

1. ***How Big Waves Impact Me*** (*Big Waves Impact Chart* handout): Students fill out the chart based on a recent personal situation after reviewing an example chart with the instructor. Provide support to help students process how a situation went, helping them see the connection between the situation (their big wave) and their thoughts, feelings, body, and resulting outcomes—negative or positive. This process can help reinforce the coping skills they used when they faced a big wave, and can be used to plan for a future storm.

2. ***My Actions and What They Can Do*** (*My Wave Actions* handout): Students complete the handout to examine their actions and behaviors and how these can impact their lives. The goal is to have students focus on the impact of their behavior. It is important that students are honest about the affect of their actions, without judgment or comment from the instructor.

3. ***Sensory Activities to Tame the Waves*** (Sensory Oral Motor—*Tame the Waves* handout): Students need a variety of powerful surfboard tools to surf during a storm, including the oral motor activities shown on the *Tame the Waves* direction sheet. Students will explore oral sensory/mouth input and how it makes them feel. Have students engage in any of the suggested oral motor activities based on known preferences or indications of interest that the student has communicated in any way. Explain that these exercises are tools that help to calm big waves of feelings and emotions.

TOPIC 4: HOW DO I RIDE OUT THE STORM?

1. ***I Can Ride Out This Storm*** (*The Waves Always Pass* handout): Students will learn and discuss how feelings and waves always pass, and how we sometimes need to tolerate the distress of a big wave because we cannot avoid it. Students will complete *The Waves Always Pass* activity sheet to experience distress tolerance for planning how to safely make it through times of big waves and emotional storms.

2. ***Tsunami Tools*** (Sensory—*Intense Sensory Exploration* handout): Students will explore preferred sensory input at greater intensity (as tolerated for each individual) shown on the *Intense Sensory Exploration* direction sheet. This activity will help students understand how to meet their sensory needs when in heightened states of arousal. SOME students will require intense sensory input. Others may need the opposite. **Honor all refusals and aversions to any intensity or input.**

3. ***Taking Charge of My Waves*** (*Self-Advocacy & My Waves* handout): Students complete the activity sheet to develop a set of self-advocacy statements that express their needs and preferences. Students then use their statements throughout the day to inform others of their needs and advocate for themselves.

TOPIC 5: HOW DO I COME BACK TO THE BEACH?

1. ***How I Surf The Waves*** (*Regulation Reminders* handout): Students will complete the activity sheet to reflect on surfing their daily waves and make plans for future surfing. This activity can be used as a quick reference resource for students, their lifeguards, and new people in their lives.

2. ***Self-Regulation Using Self-Stories*** (*Surf Story* handout): Students write their own surf story using the *Surf Story* guided process. The purpose of a surf story is to provide non-judgmental explanations to help predict and understand situations and experiences. This can reduce uncertainty and distress and improve sensory and emotional regulation. Self-stories should not be used to direct or change behavior.

3. **_Back on the Beach_** (Sensory Grounding & Calming—_Box Breathing_ handout): Students will practice box breathing patterns as they lie on towels and imagine the light and heat of the sun and listen to ocean waves. Use the _Box Breathing_ directions to complete this two-part activity. Once mastered, students can practice then use during times of dysregulation and distress.

MINDFULNESS SESSION ENDER

End each session with the following mindfulness activity.

MINDFULNESS SENSES ACTIVITY

Glitter Bottle: Students will use the glitter bottles they created in a previous activity to better understand emotions, thoughts, and behaviors.

> Tell students that the glitter represent their emotions, feelings, and thoughts. The students shake their bottles and watch as the glitter swirls around, then settles to the bottom.
>
> When the bottle is shaken, the glitter twists and turns, just as emotions and feelings do. Our emotions and feelings settle down with time, just as the glitter does. Take this time to be still and quiet and settle into a peaceful state.

Student Support: If necessary, you may make additional glitter bottles ahead of time, so that students can share them in small groups. As with any mindfulness tools, it is best for students to learn about and practice using this bottle when they are not in a heightened state of distress.

RESOURCES

Unit 5 Topic 1
Tsunamis: The
Biggest Waves

_4:00 m_

https://www.youtube.
com/watch?
v=V6cnFM55_Dw

Unit 5 Topic 1
Thunderstorms
101

_4:00 m_

https://www.youtube.
com/watch?
v=zUNEFefftt8

Unit 5 Topic 1
Surfing in a Storm

_3:00 m_

https://www.youtube.
com/watch?v=w-
CbIXBCbVU

Unit 5 Topics 1-5

Handouts

https://drive.google.com/dri
ve/folders/1e1KDwvN-
z3OzcponXuV-
zl4dZjOkxF2C?usp=drive_link

BOAT POSE

CAMEL POSE

Let's do **boat pose**:

- Sit on the floor with your legs straight out.
- Take a deep breath . . . hold . . . release.
- Lean forward and place your hands behind each knee.
- Pull your legs up toward your chest.
- Lean back and find your balance.
- Take one last deep breath . . . hold . . . release.

Let's do **camel pose**:

- Lie flat on the floor on your tummy and come up on your hands and knees.
- Take slow, deep breaths.
- Keep the top of your feet on the floor and lift yourself up on your knees.
- Look up at the sky and arch your back.
- Lean back with your arms behind your back and lay your hands on top of your heels.
- Take one last deep breath . . . hold . . . release.

STORMY WAVES

Rainstorm

Thunderstorm

Hurricane

149

STORM FORECAST

Directions: Choose at least five situations or storms that might increase your waves by filling in the box or making an X, then draw a line from each situation to the weather in the right-hand column that it might cause.

Storms That Increase My Waves

You can act like a TV weather forecaster by learning to forecast or predict when your own storms are coming. Your storms can be caused by challenging places, times of day, or situations. These storms can cause big waves, so when you predict a big storm ahead, you can prepare and use your surfboard tools.

Home Storm Forecasts:

- ☐ Getting ready for school
- ☐ Doing homework
- ☐ Ending screen time
- ☐ Coming in from playing outside
- ☐ Going to family gatherings or parties

School Storm Forecasts:

- ☐ Going back to school after vacation
- ☐ Getting ready for school
- ☐ Going back to class after lunch break
- ☐ Reading group
- ☐ Math group
- ☐ Getting a wrong answer
- ☐ Being told "no" or "stop" by teacher
- ☐ Losing free time activity
- ☐ Not getting assignment finished

Social Storm Forecasts:

- ☐ Working in a group
- ☐ Being ignored by other kids
- ☐ Getting pushed in line
- ☐ Being teased and bullied

RAINSTORM

THUNDERSTORM

HURRICANE

GLITTER BOTTLE
SENSORY ACTIVITY

MATERIALS

- **1 clear plastic bottle or jar** (e.g., 20 oz recycled bottle)
- **Glitter** (several colors and textures)
- **Warm water**
- **Glycerin or clear glue**
- **Dish soap**
- **Food coloring** (optional)
- **Duct tape or glue**
- **Small funnel**

DIRECTIONS

1. Fill the bottle two thirds full with warm water.
2. Add 1–2 tablespoons of glycerin or half a bottle of clear glue. (It slows the glitter's movement in the water. The more you add, the slower the glitter will fall.)
3. Have students choose several colors of glitter.
4. Using the funnel, add as much glitter as you feel you need.
5. Add warm water until the bottle is filled almost to the top.
6. Add 2-3 drops of dish soap.
7. Close the lid and shake. See if you need to add more glycerin or clear glue.
8. Add a small amount of food coloring, if desired.
9. Use duct tape or glue to seal the bottle.

REFLECTION QUESTIONS

Think about the following questions, then discuss with a partner or your instructor.

1. How does your glitter bottle look like a storm?
2. Did you have any storms that caused high waves and shook up your feelings today?
3. Notice how the storm in this bottle settles down. How can you help your own storms settle so your high waves pass and you feel calm and grounded?

MY EMERGENCY KIT

Directions:
Make your Emergency Kit by adding tools that will help you survive the storms that bring high waves.

You may cut and paste the tools below or you may draw or write your own (refer to *Surfboard Tools* for other examples). You can also decorate your beach bag to make it stand out!

EXAMPLES

Sensory fidgets	Breathe With the Wave card	Heavy Muscle Work: Jump or Stretch!
Headphones	Raise my hand and say, "I need help."	Get a drink of water

© Tracey DeMaria, Autism Moving Forward

EMERGENCY PLAN

Directions: Think about a storm you have had in the past—a time when your waves were high and strong. You may have been frustrated, stressed, angry, or exploding with feelings. If this happens again, what can you do to manage it better?

1. **Who could be my lifeguards next time?**

_____

_____

_____

_____

_____

2. **What activities could I do to prepare me for the storm ahead?**

_____

_____

_____

_____

_____

3. **What are five tools that might help you in this storm when your waves get stronger?**

_____

_____

_____

_____

_____

Examples: Listening to music, talking to a friend, mindful breathing, fidget tools, taking a walk, a cold drink, etc.

4. **What are three unhelpful things that might make the storm worse?**

_____

_____

_____

Examples: People talking to me when I'm upset, loud music, crowded room, too much noise and activity, my own thinking, negative thoughts, etc.

STORM CLOUDS AND STORM SCRIPTS

MATERIALS

- **Card stock or poster board**
- **Glue**
- **Paint and/or construction paper** (for background color—black, gray, white, yellow)
- **aluminum foil** (lightning bolts)
- **various small materials to be glued to the base, including:**
  - **cotton balls** (clouds & waves)
  - **black & gray pom poms**
  - **tissue paper** (clouds & waves—white, gray, black, blue)
  - **beads & glitter** (rain drops)

DIRECTIONS

Sketch or talk about what you will include in your picture and choose which materials to use.

1. Use construction paper or paint to outline the placement of clouds and other details such as lightning bolts and waves on card stock or poster board.
2. Design 3-D clouds by gluing on materials such as cotton balls, pom poms, and tissue paper.
3. Design waves under the storm clouds by gluing materials such as gray, blue, and white tissue paper.
4. Create raindrops with paint or by gluing materials such as beads or glitter.

STORM SCRIPTS

Instructor: Use the following questions to open up a discussion. Sometimes it is easier for people to discuss their feelings when they are engaged in a fun activity, instead of feeling they are on the spot in a discussion.

1. *There are times in our lives that can be challenging and stressful, making our waves of feelings and emotions larger and harder to surf. Think of a really stressful time. If that situation were an actual storm, how might it feel?* **What could you say to yourself to remain calm even when the storm is big?**

2. *When a storm is coming, how could you remind yourself to use your surfboard tools? For example, three tools you like to use are: breathing, asking for help, music. Can you think of an acronym (initials that you use to make a word) to help remember these three tools? Make a list, then take the first letter of each tool: B for Breathing, A for Asking, and M for Music. You could think of the acronym, "BAM" to remind yourself to use your surfboard tools.* **Would that help you remember?**

3. *Sometimes the storms come so fast and unexpectedly that you are unprepared. You may just need to hang on and let the waves crash over you.* **What might that feel like?**

4. *In the beginning, you may have to let the large waves crash over you, get back up on the surfboard again, and learn how to do it differently next time.* **What are some things you could say to yourself to help you remember that you can do things differently next time?**

BIG WAVES IMPACT CHART (SAMPLE)

Directions: Choose three big wave situations (something that has already caused several big waves) and fill out the chart starting at the top.

BIG WAVES THAT CAN LEAD TO STORMS

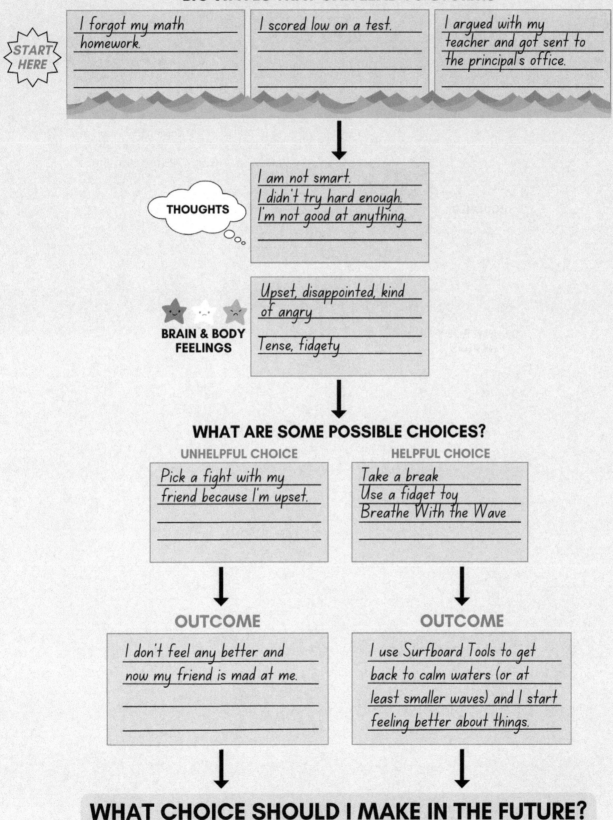

START HERE

| I forgot my math homework. | I scored low on a test. | I argued with my teacher and got sent to the principal's office. |

THOUGHTS

I am not smart.
I didn't try hard enough.
I'm not good at anything.

BRAIN & BODY FEELINGS

Upset, disappointed, kind of angry

Tense, fidgety

WHAT ARE SOME POSSIBLE CHOICES?

UNHELPFUL CHOICE

Pick a fight with my friend because I'm upset.

HELPFUL CHOICE

Take a break
Use a fidget toy
Breathe With the Wave

OUTCOME

I don't feel any better and now my friend is mad at me.

OUTCOME

I use Surfboard Tools to get back to calm waters (or at least smaller waves) and I start feeling better about things.

WHAT CHOICE SHOULD I MAKE IN THE FUTURE?

BIG WAVES IMPACT CHART

Directions: Choose three big wave situations (something that has already caused several big waves) and fill out the chart starting at the top.

BIG WAVES THAT CAN LEAD TO STORMS

START HERE

_____
_____
_____
_____

_____
_____
_____
_____

_____
_____
_____
_____

THOUGHTS

_____
_____
_____
_____

BRAIN & BODY FEELINGS

_____
_____
_____

WHAT ARE SOME POSSIBLE CHOICES?

UNHELPFUL CHOICE

_____
_____
_____
_____

HELPFUL CHOICE

_____
_____
_____
_____

OUTCOME

_____
_____
_____
_____

OUTCOME

_____
_____
_____
_____

WHAT CHOICE SHOULD I MAKE IN THE FUTURE?

MY WAVE ACTIONS

It is important to examine our actions and behaviors for the impact they can have on our feelings and waves. When we take action or behave in a way that negatively impacts ourselves or others, this can increase the size of our waves and make surfing harder. Actions and behaviors are a concern when they: make us feel worse, upset others, or are dangerous.

Directions: Read through the *Wave Situations* and think about your actions and behaviors. Then, check off at least five things in the *My Wave Actions* list that could happen when your actions are not regulated.

Wave Situations

1. My work is very hard. I get so frustrated that I rip up my assignment. I end up getting a zero.
2. I was mad that screen time was over so I threw my tablet and now I can't play on it until it is fixed.
3. When I didn't win the game, I shouted and called my best friend mean names.
4. I yelled "No!" at my favorite teacher and ran away when it was time to go back to class after P.E.
5. I am still angry about what my friend said earlier, so I walked up and kicked them in the leg.
6. I threw markers when I didn't want to clean up and they hit my classmates and teacher.

My Wave Actions

- [ ] Hurt someone's feelings
- [ ] Make someone else have bad body or brain feelings
- [ ] Break something
- [ ] Hurt or injure myself
- [ ] Hurt or injure someone else
- [ ] Make more work for myself
- [ ] Make it harder for me to learn
- [ ] Make it hard for me to play with friends
- [ ] Missing out on something fun
- [ ] Disappointing someone I care about
- [ ] Feeling worse in my brain or body

TAME THE WAVES
SENSORY ACTIVITY

MATERIALS

- Various sized straws for blowing light objects
- Light objects: cotton balls, pom poms, ping pong balls, tiny rolled paper balls
- Bubble solution and wands
- Whistles and kazoos
- Pinwheel or wind spinner

DIRECTIONS

Oral motor activities are powerful surfboard tools. Have students engage in oral sensory and motor activities based on their preferences known or communicated in any way.

1. Students use straws to blow light objects across a desk, table, or floor. Increase the challenge by having students:
   - Blow items along a marked path.
   - Blow items without a straw.
2. Demonstrate and have students imitate using various bubble wands and solution to:
   - Blow bubbles in different sizes.
   - Use different breathing patterns.
3. Students use a straw to blow and create bubbles or waves in a tub or large bowl filled with water.
   - Note: Follow safety guidelines to change the water and sanitize tubs or bowls for each student.
4. Students blow into instruments to make sounds (e.g., whistles, kazoos, harmonicas, and any other mouth instruments).
   - Note. Use low noise whistles to limit noise and possible distress (e.g., lip shaped whistles are quiet and affordable).
5. Demonstrate how to blow and activate a pinwheel or wind spinner and then have students take turns blowing and activating the items. This also provides nice visual sensory input.

OPTIONAL ACTIVITIES

Additional oral sensory/motor tools for those students who cannot master blowing. Start with oral motor exercises to increase deep pressure (e.g., puffing cheeks, pursing lips, squeezing lips together, pushing tongue into cheeks). Present other items to students to explore and to observe students' reaction and discuss what they liked and didn't like to determine if these are good surfboard tools to use.

1. Ice or other frozen items
2. Sour and/or spicy foods (lemon, vinegar, salsa, wasabi peas)
3. Crunchy food (carrots, hard pretzels, tortilla chips)
4. Gum, chewy food (bagels, jerky, dried fruit)
5. Vibrating toothbrush

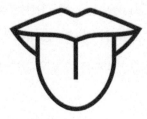

THE WAVES ALWAYS PASS

Directions: Read and review *The Waves Always Pass* passage below. Complete the following chart by listing specific activities that can be used for distress tolerance during times of increasingly large waves.

The Waves Always Pass: Some big wave situations are genuinely distressing and may come up unexpectedly. If we can't plan and be prepared for the situation or if the wave is just too big for us to surf right now, sometimes all we can do is brace ourselves and let the waves crash over us. We get back up on our surfboard and try again. Knowing that all waves eventually pass is an important part of getting through the hard times.

Activity & Input	When & Where to Use It	How It Makes Me Feel
Mindful breathing	Can be used anywhere before and during distress	Calmer, better able to cope

Preferred Activities to Help Me Regulate

Distracting activities—video games, cooking, science experiments, and other hands-on activities.

Sensory activities—Items that either soothe or stimulate to change the state of my nervous system. Consider intense sensory input.

Emergency Kit—special interest items, favorite books, pictures, toys, sensory tools, candy, or treats.

Relaxation exercises—Mindfulness activities and breathing exercises.

Eating—foods with texture (soft, crunchy), favorite foods and drinks.

Exercise—Physical activity in any form.

Water—taking a bath or shower, hands in water.

INTENSE SENSORY EXPLORATION

Instructor: Students will explore preferred sensory inputs at a higher intensity, as tolerated. The point of this is to help students meet their sensory needs when in heightened states of arousal, which can require intensity. For SOME students this will require intense sensory input. Others may need the opposite. **Honor all refusals and aversions to any intensity.**

MATERIALS

- Ice or other frozen items
- Sour foods (lemon) and sour candy
- Spicy foods
- Music with fast tempo (strong bass, guitar, drums)

DIRECTIONS

Have students explore as many of the following as possible. Students can indicate what they like and what might help during the big waves that can lead to storms. If not available, use pictures and discuss more intense sensory options.

1. Touching or holding ice cube
2. Chewing ice chips
3. Splashing cold water on face or hands
4. Eating spicy or sour food item
5. Listening to loud music or intense music with strong beat or fast tempo (maintain ear health safety volume)
6. Push-ups/wall push-ups
7. Running fast
8. Jumping up and down in place for 20-30 seconds
9. Squeeze hands closed very tight for 5 seconds—let go and repeat
10. Big and/or repetitive movements (rocking, jumping, flapping, pacing, arm circles, etc.)

Student: Make a list of the Intense Sensory Tools that work best for you.

MY INTENSE SENSORY TOOLS

_____

_____

_____

_____

_____

INTENSE SENSORY EXPLORATION

MY INTENSE SENSORY TOOLS

_____

_____

_____

_____

_____

© Tracey DeMaria, Autism Moving Forward

Name:

MY INTENSE SENSORY TOOLS

_____

_____

_____

_____

_____

© Tracey DeMaria, Autism Moving Forward

Name:

MY INTENSE SENSORY TOOLS

_____

_____

_____

_____

© Tracey DeMaria, Autism Moving Forward

Name:

SELF-ADVOCACY & MY WAVES

Directions: Review statements below and identify any you can use to advocate for yourself. Come up with three of your own advocacy statements. You can carry these cards with you to use throughout the day. It is important to have control over what happens to you and ask for what you need to feel regulated in your brain and body.

I need help

I need a break

I need _____ right now!

Please don't force eye contact

Please do not touch me

I am overwhelmed

Please give me space

I need more time to process this

I need to speak to _____ (lifeguard)

162

REGULATION REMINDERS

Name: _____

Directions: Use what you've learned about waves, surfing, and surfboard tools, and list items that serve as triggers, helpers, regulators, and safety measures.

My Waves

My Surfboard Tools

My Lifeguards

My Sharks

My Storm Kit

SURF STORY (SAMPLE)

Directions: The purpose of a *Surf Story* is to provide non-judgmental explanations to help predict and understand situations and experiences in order to reduce uncertainty and distress and improve sensory and emotional regulation. **They should not be used to direct or change behavior.**

Note: These stories can also be done on a computer with pictures added. Answering each question on a separate page makes a nice book that can be read over and over to help prepare for situations that create anxiety or uncertainty.

Using the following questions, write a *Surf Story* about predicting a situation or event that is likely to cause you to have big waves, such as taking a test or speaking in front of the class. Be as creative as you want and use kind words about yourself when writing your Surf Story. You can ask an adult for help.

Questions	My *Surf Story*
1. What is the situation or event that I will be facing?	I have to take a test in a few days. It feels like a big storm with lots of big waves.
2. How do my brain and body feel about the situation or event?	My brain is feeling very nervous and my body feels tight. My belly feels funny and my head feels swimmy.
3. What tools do I know work for me when I am having big wave feelings?	My favorite surfboard tools are to run and play outside, do my stretches, listen to music, have a crunchy or sour snack to eat. I can also use my affirmations, wave breathing, and distract myself by watching my favorite TV show.
4. What worried thoughts and unhelpful actions can make my waves bigger in this situation or event?	I keep thinking about what I will do wrong on the test when the teacher mentions it. Also, when I talk about the test a lot, it makes me keep thinking about it and it makes the waves bigger.
5. What lifeguard can help me manage the waves in this situation or event?	I can ask my teacher, a parent, or my other lifeguards to help me remember to use my surfboard tools and to help me surf my waves if they get too big.
6. What other information about the situation or event will I need to prepare for?	When the test day comes, I will probably be nervous and stressed. That is OK. My mind and body can feel waves and surf them. I am not in danger, and I am not going to be in trouble. I will get through this test. I always do. If I prepared and I try my best that is all I need to do. If it feels too hard, I can take my time and ask for help if I get confused.

SURF STORY

Directions: The purpose of a *Surf Story* is to provide non-judgmental explanations to help predict and understand situations and experiences in order to reduce uncertainty and distress and improve sensory and emotional regulation. **They should not be used to direct or change behavior.**

Note: These stories can also be done on a computer with pictures added. Answering each question on a separate page makes a nice book that can be read over and over to help prepare for situations that create anxiety or uncertainty.

Using the following questions, write a story about predicting a situation or event that is likely to cause you to have big waves, such as taking a test or speaking in front of the class. Be as creative as you want and use kind words about yourself when writing your *Surf Story*. You can ask an adult for help.

Questions	My *Surf Story*
1. What is the situation or event that I will be facing?	
2. How do my brain and body feel about the situation or event?	
3. What tools do I know work for me when I am having big wave feelings?	
4. What worried thoughts and unhelpful actions can make my waves bigger in this situation or event?	
5. What lifeguard can help me manage the waves in this situation or event?	
6. What other information about the situation or event will I need to prepare for?	

BOX BREATHING
GROUNDING & CALMING ACTIVITY

Students will practice box breathing patterns as they lie on their towels and imagine the light and heat of the sun as they listen to ocean waves. This activity is two parts and is excellent to practice then use during times of dysregulation and distress once mastered.

MATERIALS

- Towels
- Ocean wave sounds
- Box Breathing graphic

DIRECTIONS

This activity is two parts and is excellent to practice for use during times of dysregulation and distress, once mastered.

1. First, have students look at the *Box Breathing* graphic and practice the breathing pattern with cues for timing and modeling.
2. Once they are familiar with this breathing pattern, instruct students to lie on their towels and listen to the ocean waves. As they get comfortable, instruct them to begin box breathing, counting the seconds silently in their heads.
3. As they get into the box breathing pattern, instruct them to imagine the light and heat of the sun warming their body. They should do this for two minutes.

Note: Explain that this breathing can be used any time they need it. They do not need to close their eyes or lay down for box breathing to help with calming and regulation.

Box Breathing Directions

1. Start by breathing in and slowly counting to four.
2. With your lungs comfortably full, hold your breath for four seconds.
3. Slowly breathe out by taking a slow, full breath while counting to four.
4. Hold your breath and count to four with no air in your lungs.
5. Repeat sequence breathing in and out for four seconds.

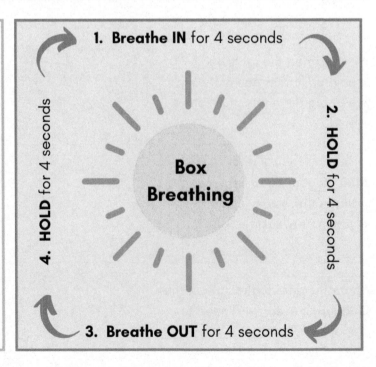

1. **Breathe IN** for 4 seconds
2. **HOLD** for 4 seconds
3. **Breathe OUT** for 4 seconds
4. **HOLD** for 4 seconds

Box Breathing

REFERENCES

Amundsen, R., Riby, L. M., Hamilton, C., Hope, M., & McGann, D. (2020). Mindfulness in primary school children as a route to enhanced life satisfaction, positive outlook and effective emotion regulation. *BMC Psychology, 8*(1), 71. https://doi.org/10.1186/s40359-020-00428-y

Ayres, A. J. (1972). *Sensory integration and learning disorders.* Los Angeles, CA: Western Psychological Services.

Ayres, A. J. (1979). *Sensory integration and the child.* Los Angeles, CA: Western Psychological Services.

Baldwin, J. (2020). *Narrative therapy to reduce self-stigma: Empowering children, adolescents, and their families.* [Doctoral dissertation, University of Denver]. Digital Commons @ DU. https://digitalcommons.du.edu/capstone_masters/389/

Bremner, J. D. (2022). Traumatic stress: Effects on the brain. *Dialogues in Clinical Neuroscience, 8*(4), 445-461. https://doi.org/10.31887/DCNS.2006.8.4/jbremner

Brown, A., Tse, T., & Fortune, T. (2019). Defining sensory modulation: A review of the concept and a contemporary definition for application by occupational therapists. *Scandinavian Journal of Occupational Therapy, 26*(7), 515-523. https://doi.org/10.1080/11038128.2018.1509370

Bundy, A. C., Lane, S., Murray, E. A., & Fisher, A. G. (2002). *Sensory integration: Theory and practice* (2nd ed). Philadelphia: F.A. Davis.

Chamoun, E., Mutch, D. M., Allen-Vercoe, E., Buchholz, A. C., Duncan, A. M., Spriet, L. L., Haines, J., Ma, D. W. L., & Guelph Family Health Study. (2018). A review of the associations between single nucleotide polymorphisms in taste receptors, eating behaviors, and health. *Critical Reviews in Food Science and Nutrition, 58*(2), 194-207. https://doi.org/10.1080/10408398.2016.1152229

Communication Theory. (n.d.) *Arousal theory.* Retrieved April 30, 2022, from https://www.communicationtheory.org/arousal-theory/

Davison, K., Bowling, A., Garcia, J., Wood, B., Hermesch, R., Prince, J., Hayes, A., Kow, R., Newlan, S., & Slavet, J. (2016). A cybercycling intervention to improve behavioral regulation and classroom functioning among children with behavioral health disorders: Pragmatic randomized trial design for Manville Moves. *Contemporary Clinical Trials, 49*, 40-46. https://doi.org/10.1016/j.cct.2016.05.008

De Bellis, M. D., & Zisk, A. (2014). The biological effects of childhood trauma. *Child and Adolescent Psychiatric Clinics of North America, 23*(2), 185-222. https://doi.org/10.1016/j.chc.2014.01.002

Dumornay, N. M., Lebois, L. A., Ressler, K. J., & Harnett, N. G. (2023). Racial disparities in adversity during childhood and the false appearance of race-related differences in brain structure. *American Journal of Psychiatry, 180*(2), 127-138. https://doi.org/10.1176/appi.ajp.21090961

English, R., Campbell, M., & Moir, L. (2023) Deschooling and unschooling after experiences of bullying: Five parents tell their stories. *Journal of Unschooling and Alternative Learning, 17*(33), pp. 1-25. https://eprints.qut.edu.au/238245/

Felver, J. C., Celis-de Hoyos, C. E., Tezanos, K., & Singh, N. N. (2016). A systematic review of mindfulness-based interventions for youth in school settings. *Mindfulness, 7*(1), 34-45. https://doi.org/10.1007/s12671-015-0389-4

Flook, L., Smalley, S. L., Kitil, M. J., Galla, B. M., Kaiser-Greenland, S., Locke, J., Ishijima, E., & Kasari, C. (2010). Effects of mindful awareness practices on executive functions in elementary school children. *Journal of Applied School Psychology, 26*(1), 70-95. https://doi.org/10.1080/15377900903379125

Garey, J. (2022, November 10.) *DBT: What Is dialectical behavior therapy? A treatment for teenagers with serious trouble managing emotions.* Child Mind Institute. https://childmind.org/article/dbt-dialectical-behavior-therapy/

Goldin, P. R., & Gross, J. J. (2010). Effects of mindfulness-based stress reduction (MBSR) on emotion regulation in social anxiety disorder. *Emotion, 10*(1), 83-91. https://doi.org/10.1037/a0018441

Greene, R. W. (2010). *Collaborative problem solving: The model and its application across settings.* New York: Guilford.

Grossman, A., & Avital, A. (2023). Emotional and sensory dysregulation as a possible missing link in attention deficit hyperactivity disorder: A review. *Frontiers in Behavioral Neuroscience, 17*, 1118937. https://doi.org/10.3389/fnbeh.2023.1118937

Hancock, S., & Richardson, S. C. (2022.) Curriculum-induced trauma: Trauma-informed models and schools as the trauma inducing agent. *Journal of Trauma Studies in Education, 1*(3), 122-134. https://doi.org/10.32674/jtse.v1i3.5057

Hendricks, M. A., & Buchanan, T. W. (2016). Individual differences in cognitive control processes and their relationship to emotion regulation. *Cognition and Emotion, 30*(5), 912-924. https://doi.org/10.1080/02699931.2015.1032893

Hochberg, Z. (2011). Developmental plasticity in child growth and maturation. *Frontiers in Endocrinology, 2*. https://doi.org/10.3389/fendo.2011.00041

Immordino-Yang, M. H., & Singh, V. (2013). Hippocampal contributions to the processing of social emotions. *Human Brain Mapping, 34*(4), 945-955. https://doi.org/10.1002/hbm.21485

Kamraju, M. (2023.) The impact of yoga on mental health. *Indonesian Journal of Community and Special Needs Education, 3*(2), 141-146. https://doi.org/10.17509/ijcsne.v3i2.57747

Kerns, C. M., Lankenau, S., Shattuck, P. T., Robins, D. L., Newschaffer, C. J., & Berkowitz, S. J. (2022). Exploring potential sources of childhood trauma: A qualitative study with autistic adults and caregivers. *Autism, 26*(8), 1987-1998. https://doi.org/10.1177/13623613211070637

Kiecolt-Glaser, J. K., Christian, L., Preston, H., Houts, C. R., Malarkey, W. B., Emery, C. F., & Glaser, R. (2010). Stress, inflammation, and yoga practice. *Psychosomatic Medicine, 72*(2), 113-121. https://doi.org/10.1097/PSY.0b013e3181cb9377

Kilroy, E., Aziz-Zadeh, L., & Cermak, S. (2019). Ayres theories of autism and sensory integration revisited: What contemporary neuroscience has to say. *Brain Sciences, 9*(3), 68. https://doi.org/10.3390/brainsci9030068

Lane, S. J., Mailloux, Z., Schoen, S., Bundy, A., May-Benson, T. A., Parham, L. D., Smith Roley, S., & Schaaf, R. C. (2019). Neural foundations of Ayres Sensory Integration®. *Brain Sciences, 9*(7), 153. https://doi.org/10.3390/brainsci9070153

Lau Zhu, A., & Mann, J. (2023). "I'm a man now": Using Narrative Therapy to support an adult with Down syndrome transition to a new life. *British Journal of Learning Disabilities.* https://doi.org/10.1111/bld.12526

Lee, V., Roudbarani, F., Tablon Modica, P., Pouyandeh, A., & Weiss, J. A. (2022). Adaptation of cognitive behavior therapy for autistic children during the pandemic: A mixed-methods program evaluation. *Evidence-Based Practice in Child and Adolescent Mental Health, 7*(1), 76-93. https://doi.org/10.1080/23794925.2021.1941432

Mahler, K. (2015). *Interoception: The eighth sensory system.* Lenexa, KS: AAPC Publishing.

Nicholson, H., Kehle, T. J., Bray, M. A., & Van Heest, J. (2011). The effects of antecedent physical activity on the academic engagement of children with autism spectrum disorder. *Psychology in the Schools, 48*(2), 198-213. https://doi.org/10.1002/pits.20537

Norcross, J. C., VandenBos, G. R., Freedheim, D. K., & Olatunji, B. O. (Eds.). (2016). *APA handbook of clinical psychology: Theory and research (Vol. 2).* American Psychological Association. https://doi.org/10.1037/14773-000

Nurius, P. S., & Macy, R. J. (2008). Cognitive behavioral theory. In Sowers, K. M., & Dulmus, C. N. (Eds.), *Comprehensive Handbook of Social Work and Social Welfare, Human Behavior in the Social Environment* (pp. 101-132). John Wiley & Sons.

Oriel, K. N., George, C. L., Peckus, R., & Semon, A. (2011). The effects of aerobic exercise on academic engagement in young children with autism spectrum disorder. *Pediatric Physical Therapy, 23*(2), 187-193. https://doi.org/10.1097/PEP.0b013e318218f149

Patten Koenig, K., & Hough Williams, L. (2017). Characterization and utilization of preferred interests: A survey of adults on the autism spectrum. *Occupational Therapy in Mental Health, 33*(2), 129-140. https://doi.org/10.1080/0164212X.2016.1248877

Paulus, F. W., Ohmann, S., Möhler, E., Plener, P., & Popow, C. (2021). Emotional dysregulation in children and adolescents with psychiatric disorders. A narrative review. *Frontiers in Psychiatry, 12*, 628252. https://doi.org/10.3389/fpsyt.2021.628252

Peverill, M., Rosen, M. L., Lurie, L. A., Sambrook, K. A., Sheridan, M. A., & McLaughlin, K. A. (2023). Childhood trauma and brain structure in children and adolescents. *Developmental Cognitive Neuroscience, 59*, 101180. https://doi.org/10.1016/j.dcn.2022.101180

Powell, T. M. (2020). *The scars of suspension: Testimonies as narratives of school-induced collective trauma* [Doctoral dissertation, University of California, Los Angeles]. UCLA. https://escholarship.org/uc/item/05p4b41r

RajMohan, V., & Mohandas, E. (2007). The limbic system. *Indian Journal of Psychiatry, 49*(2), 132. https://doi.org/10.4103/0019-5545.33264

Rolls, E. T. (2019). The cingulate cortex and limbic systems for emotion, action, and memory. *Brain Structure and Function, 224*(9), 3001-3018. https://doi.org/10.1007/s00429-019-01945-2

Santucci, G. (2023). *Upstairs brain.* Greg Santucci. https://gregsantucci.com/infographic/upstairs-brain/

Schaaf, R. C., & Miller, L. J. (2005). Occupational therapy using a sensory integrative approach for children with developmental disabilities. *Mental Retardation and Developmental Disabilities Research Reviews, 11*(2), 143-148. https://doi.org/10.1002/mrdd.20067

Schonert-Reichl, K. A., Oberle, E., Lawlor, M. S., Abbott, D., Thomson, K., Oberlander, T. F., & Diamond, A. (2015). Enhancing cognitive and social-emotional development through a simple-to-administer mindfulness-based school program for elementary school children: A randomized controlled trial. *Developmental Psychology, 51*(1), 52-66. https://doi.org/10.1037/a0038454

Selvanathan, J., Pham, C., Nagappa, M., Peng, P. W., Englesakis, M., Espie, C. A., Morin, C. M., & Chung, F. (2021). Cognitive behavioral therapy for insomnia in patients with chronic pain-A systematic review and meta-analysis of randomized controlled trials. *Sleep Medicine Reviews, 60*, 101460. https://doi.org/10.1016/j.smrv.2021.101460

Sowa, M., & Meulenbroek, R. (2012). Effects of physical exercise on autism spectrum disorders: A meta-analysis. *Research in Autism Spectrum Disorders, 6*(1), 46-57. https://doi.org/10.1016/j.rasd.2011.09.001

STAR Institute. (n.d.) *Your 8 senses.* Sensory Health. Retrieved August 21, 2023, from https://sensoryhealth.org/basic/your-8-senses

Zantinge, G., van Rijn, S., Stockmann, L., & Swaab, H. (2017). Physiological arousal and emotion regulation strategies in young children with autism spectrum disorders. *Journal of Autism and Developmental Disorders, 47*(9), 2648-2657. https://doi.org/10.1007/s10803-017-3181-6

ACKNOWLEDGEMENTS

This book stands as a testament to the collective effort, wisdom, and continual advancement of occupational therapists and educators everywhere. I extend my deepest gratitude to the pioneers in sensory integration, occupational therapy, and psychology, whose foundational work laid the groundwork for the activities found within this book. Special thanks to Anita Bundy, ScD, OTR, FAOTA, Lois Hickman, MS, OTR, FAOTA, Tracy Murnan Stackhouse, MA, OTR, and Ellen MacLaughlin, Ed.D., OTR/L, FAOTA, for your personal mentorship. Endless gratitude to Roger and Jill for being skilled lifeguards and sharing your wisdom.

I am eternally grateful to my editors and the creative team at AMF—Rebecca, Ruth, Erin, and René. You each deserve special acknowledgment for your dedication and innovative spirit, which transformed conceptual notions into the tangible reality of this user-friendly program. I can't thank you enough for your belief in me and continuous support.

My deepest gratitude and respect for the many families, children, and individuals with whom I have worked over the years, and who have trusted me to be part of their journey. It is through bearing witness to dysregulation that I have been able to hone my understanding of how to best promote and support regulation.

Much love and appreciation to my friends and colleagues, especially my Phillipsburg School District crew, whose support and valuable insights over the years were instrumental in the development of this project.

My family has been a guiding force, each one navigating their own life's waves and contributing to my understanding of the continuous journey to improvement. A special thanks to my visionary sister, Christine Sutton-Ryan, whose creativity ignited the inception of this program; Julianne, for your unwavering support and belief in me as my first surfing partner; Mom and Pop, for always loving me and being there when I need you. For my nieces and nephews, keep surfing those waves.

My dearest Miles—thank you for bringing my surfing knowledge up to speed. You continue to be my greatest teacher. By bravely sharing your experiences of being autistic, you inspire me to unlearn the old and relearn how to best support neurodivergent individuals and to provide meaningful resources to others. Finally, Christopher, thank you for always believing in me, for loving me completely, and for keeping me going in every way through it all. You are my ultimate co-regulating lifeguard. Miip .

ABOUT THE AUTHOR

Tracey DeMaria, OTD, OTR/L, is an occupational therapist with a lifelong dedication to promoting sensory and emotional regulation. After studying occupational therapy at Colorado State University, Tracey's passion for helping children and adults play, grow, and flourish led her to work in various clinic and farm-based occupational therapy settings, where she discovered the transformative power of music and animals. She founded and directed the Sensation Whole Child Center, LLC, where she honed her skills through advanced training and clinical work. Tracey's commitment to supporting parents of children with disabilities has led her to host advocacy groups, run therapy groups and camps, and provide educational advocacy. She has a doctorate in occupational therapy and is an adjunct professor at Moravian University in Pennsylvania.

Tracey resides in Easton, PA, where she cherishes spending time with her husband, son, and their two dogs, Max and Navigator. As a proud neurodivergent individual, Tracey is dedicated to helping people of all ages and neurotypes understand the profound impact of sensory and emotional regulation. Her work as a clinician, professor, and advocate continues to make a positive difference in the lives of individuals and communities alike.

Autism Moving Forward Publishing

From the Publisher

Dear Readers,

We hope you enjoyed *How to Surf the Waves*. To enhance your experience with the curriculum, we've made the lesson handouts and worksheets easily accessible. You can find them online by using the QR code.

For additional guidance and support, including educational *How to Surf the Waves* videos, visit **www.traceydemaria.com** or follow on YouTube: **www.youtube.com/@traceydemaria**.

But that's not all! We invite you to check out another publication by AMF Publishing, *Life After Lockdown: Resetting Perceptions of Autism*. This thought-provoking work encourages embracing autistic individuals for their unique qualities, fostering a perspective that sees people defined by their abilities, not limitations. Discover proven strategies and insights from a diverse group of neurodiverse and neurotypical experts. Empower individuals, families, and educators to create a supportive environment that helps autistic individuals thrive across the lifespan.

You can also find more valuable resources by visiting **www.autismmovingforward.com**, or by browsing our offerings on TeachersPayTeachers. Don't forget to connect with us on social media!

  @autismmovingforward

Thank you for choosing *How to Surf the Waves*. We are excited to be part of your journey in supporting emotional regulation and embracing neurodiversity.

Warm regards,

The AMF Publishing Team

Printed in Great Britain
by Amazon

41071857R00104